Key Stage 2

Practice

Carol Matchett

Name _____

Schofield & Sims

Introduction

Understanding English Practice lets you practise aspects of the English curriculum: grammar, punctuation, vocabulary, spelling, fiction, non-fiction and poetry. All of these topics are linked: what you learn in grammar, punctuation, vocabulary and spelling will help you to understand and communicate more effectively when reading and writing fiction, non-fiction and poetry texts.

How to use this book

Before you start using this book, write your name in the name box on the first page.

Then decide how to begin. If you want to practise your grammar, for example, you should work through the grammar section from beginning to end. If you just want to practise a particular topic, such as sentence structure, then choose the relevant pages from that section.

Whichever way you choose, don't try to do too much at once – it's better to tackle the questions in short bursts.

For help with any of the topics, look at the box at the bottom of each page:

> **For help with the questions on this page see**
> *Understanding English: Grammar* **pages 4–8.**

This tells you which of the **Understanding English** study books will help you and where in those books to find the relevant help.

Answers

Answers to the questions can be found at the end of the book (pages 74–92). Use this section to help you to mark your work as you go along. Sometimes there is more than one possible answer to a question. In this case the Answers section provides example answers which will help you to mark your work.

Make a note of any questions or topics you found difficult and use the **Understanding English** study books to help you with these.

Contents

Tick the box when you have worked through the topic.

Grammar Nouns and adjectives

1 Write a more **precise noun** for each one in **bold**. Underline the other **nouns** in these sentences.

a The **man** went for a run in the park.

✓ The jogger went for a run

b An angry woman chased her dog around the **shop**.

✓ The angry woman chased her dog around the library.

c Mr Brown left his book in the **room**.

✓ Mr Brown left his book in the study.

d The **lady** put her new case on the seat of her car.

Mummy put her new case on the sea of her car.

e His story about my dog eating the **cake** was a lie.

His story about my dog eating the wedding cake was a lie. ✓

2 Add an **adjective** to give more detail about each **noun**.

a a __big__ (*Pale, strange, fierce*) face behind a __narow__ (*narrow ✓*) window

b a pair of __∅ white__ slippers in front of the __rageing__ (✓) fire

c a __wett wet__ day in __a graty__ (*foggy, dull, damp*) (*grotty*) November

d a __cnvant__ cottage in a __Small__ village

3 Underline all the **determiners** in this sentence.

There was some bread in the basket and a juicy apple.

4 Complete this sentence using **two adjectives** and **two precise nouns**.

The castle had _____

5 Complete this sentence using a **comparative adjective**.

Scarface the pirate _____ .

6 Complete this sentence using **three superlatives**.

This ice cream _____ .

Grammar Verbs and adverbs

1 Complete these sentences with **verbs** that make sense.

   a The getaway car ___skidded___ left and ___crashed___ to a halt.

   b The flood water ___rushed___ past him as he ___swam___ against it.

   c I ___jumped___ out of bed and ___took___ myself to the bathroom.

   d She ___tripped / tripped___ up the slope as a rock ___tumbled___ tumble past her.

   e Yannis ___dribbled___ through the defence and ___tossed___ the ball into the net.

2 Rewrite these sentences with an **adverb** to describe *how* the actions were performed.

   a Jameela opened the box.

     Jameela opened the box CAREFULLY
     Jameela was opening the Box

   b He held on.

     He held on TIGHTLY
     He was holding on

   c He gathered up his papers.

     He gathered up his papers QUICKLY
     He was gathering up his papers

   d She sat down.

     She sat down SLOWLY
     She was sitting down

   e That night he slept.

     That night he slept RESTLESSLY
     That night he was sleeping

3 Add a suitable **adverb** to the start of these sentences.

   a ___hasterly___ he clambered over the wall.

   b ___Quickly___ CAREFULLY / SLOWLY add the milk to the mixture.

   c ___silently___ Greedily? he ate the last slice.

   d ___gradually___ Gently? the snow fell during the night.

4 Change the **verbs** in these sentences to the **past tense**.

   a The squirrel is startled and races up the tree.

   b The old man eats his dinner and washes up.

   c Leaves fall from the trees and flutter in the breeze.

For help with the questions on this page see
Understanding English: Grammar pages 10–13.

1 **a** Everyone needs clean water. After all, we cannot live without it.

What is the purpose of the words 'After all'? _____

b Many countries, however, face severe water shortages.

Which word shows that this sentence follows the previous sentence? _____

2 Add a suitable **time adverbial** to link the events. Don't use the word 'then'.

a Ellie searched the house. _____ Max waited outside.

b He stepped into the dungeon. _____ the door slammed shut.

c The knight rode for many days. _____ he reached the castle walls.

d The well was not used. _____ the villagers forgot about it.

e Sieve the flour into the bowl. _____ stir in the sugar.

3 Write a second sentence linked by the **adverbial**.

a Sarai was trapped in the cellar. However, _____.

b Some animals are endangered. On the other hand, _____.

c Kyle was exhausted. In contrast, _____.

4 Write a second sentence to show the **result** of these events. Use an **adverbial** to link the two sentences.

a Gale force winds battered the country last night. _____

_____

b It has not rained for a month. _____

_____

> For help with the questions on this page see
> *Understanding English: Grammar* pages 22–23.

1 Choose a suitable **conjunction** to introduce the subordinate c

    a He could not go home _____ he desperately wanted to.

    b He could not go home _____ he did not know the way.

    c He could not go home _____ he found the key.

    d He could not go home _____ the storm was raging.

    e He could not go home _____ everything he had said.

2   **a** Underline the **conjunctions** in this sentence.

    The old gentleman smiled when he saw the photograph because it reminded him of happier times.

    b Tick the sentence that uses 'before' as a **subordinating conjunction**.

    The old gentleman smiled before he left.   ☐

    The old gentleman left before me.   ☐

    The old gentleman arrived before midday.   ☐

3 Choose a different **conjunction** from the box to help you complete each sentence.

before	until	although	unless	if	but

    a She left the safety of the cave _____.

    b The rumble grew louder and louder _____.

    c There was no way out _____.

    d He wiped his eyes _____.

    e He would open the chest _____.

    f The desert seemed endless _____.

For help with the questions on this page see
Understanding English: Grammar **page 18.**

Grammar Verb tense and agreement

1 Complete this sentence using the **past progressive form** of the verbs 'watch' and 'talk'.

I _____ television while Mum _____ on the phone.

2 The **verbs** in these sentences are wrong. Write the correct version of each sentence.

a On Friday we catched the bus. _____

b Tomorrow I was up early. _____

c He throwed the ball to me. _____

d He had eat already. _____

e The window was broked. _____

3 Read these sentences. Check if all the verbs are in the right **tense**. Underline and correct the mistakes.

a All last week the car is being repaired so we have to walk. _____ _____

b Yesterday, we met Mick and go to the park before it rains. _____ _____

c Saturday was a stormy day so Beth stays indoors and reads. _____ _____

d We found the castle but it is closed, so we come straight back. _____ _____

4 The wrong **form** of verb has been used in these sentences. Underline the mistakes and write each sentence correctly.

a I has brown hair. _____

b We was really sorry. _____

c These buses is always late. _____

d I likes football. _____

e There was people everywhere. _____

For help with the questions on this page see
Understanding English: Grammar **pages 24–25 and 28.**

Grammar Person and pronouns

1 Add **pronouns** to complete these sentences.

   a They were waiting for _____ mother to pick _____ up from swimming.

   b I knew the bag was _____ because _____ saw _____ name in it.

2 These sentences are written in the **first person**. Change the **pronouns** so they are in the **third person**.

   a The dog was right behind me as I ran towards my front gate.

   b We only moved into our new house a week ago, and moving to the country has been a shock for us all.

3 What does the pronoun 'It' refer to in the second sentence below?

Jack and I are really stuck with this problem. **It** is very difficult.

_____

4 This text has too many pronouns. Rewrite it changing some of the pronouns to **nouns** or **names** so the meaning is clear.

> Ezra took his dog Rex for a walk in the park. He threw a stick and he bounded after it, wagging his tail. He stopped and sniffed around the bush where it had landed, but then he forgot about it and set off again. This time he did not stop. He shouted for him to come back – but he just kept running.

_____

_____

_____

_____

_____

_____.

For help with the questions on this page see
Understanding English: Grammar pages 16–17 and 26–27.

1 Write a **one-clause sentence** using the word given.

a clock   → _____

b chocolate → _____

c swung   → _____

d groaned → _____

e time   → _____

2 Write a one-clause sentence to follow the one given.

a The thief has not been found. _____

b Ben did not hear. _____

3 Use the conjunctions **and**, **but**, **or** to complete these sentences.

a I looked around _____ the house was empty _____ silent.

b He must stay calm _____ concentrate _____ he would make a mistake.

4 Complete these sentences by adding another **main clause**.

a The dog barked and _____ .

b The dog barked but _____ .

c At first she seemed friendly but _____ .

d He pointed a trembling finger and _____ .

e Switch the lights off or _____ .

5 Underline the **subject** of each sentence.

a Jenny fell off a wall.   **c** The dog hid the bone.

b The box was on the table.   **d** We went to the cinema.

For help with the questions on this page see
Understanding English: Grammar pages 33–34.

Grammar Adverbials

1 Complete these sentences, using **prepositional phrases** to show when and where the events happened.

a A fire had started _____.

b A thick fog descended _____.

c The two strangers walked together _____.

d _____ the boy sat quietly _____.

e _____ he found an enormous pumpkin _____.

f _____ the King called his advisers _____.

2 Choose one of your sentences from above and add an **adverb** to say how the event happened. Write the new complete sentence.

_____

3 Each of these sentences contains an adverb and a prepositional phrase. Rewrite each sentence with the adverb or prepositional phrase, or both, at the start of the sentence.

a There was a sack of gold outside behind the dustbins.

_____

b He slowly raised his hand to the sky.

_____

c The crowd gathered excitedly outside the palace.

_____

d A figure emerged gradually from the purple smoke.

_____

e Snow fell silently during the night.

_____

For help with the questions on this page see
Understanding English: Grammar **pages 12–15 and 40.**

Grammar Clauses

1 Use **conjunctions** to combine the information from three simple sentences into **one sentence**.

a The lamp failed. He tried the torch. It just flickered and died.

_____

b He picked up the spade. He dug and dug. He was exhausted.

_____

c They fled the city. They rode for seven nights. They reached safety.

_____

2 **a** Underline the **main clause** in this sentence.

Mrs Brown gripped her hat, which nearly blew away.

b Underline the subordinate clause in this sentence.

Mary hurried to school even when it snowed.

c Underline the relative clause in this sentence.

The house that was for sale was rather run down.

3 Write a **two-** or **three-clause sentence** to follow each of these short sentences.

a The tiger paused. _____

_____

b Time was running out. _____

_____

c Lightning flashed. _____

_____

d He wept for joy. _____

_____

For help with the questions on this page see
Understanding English: Grammar pages 35–37 and 42.

Practice

1 Rewrite these sentences with the **subordinate clause** at the start.

a He took shelter inside when the rain came.

_____

b The library will close next month unless we do something.

_____

c I strode to the front of the class although I was nervous.

_____

d The room fell silent as the magician appeared.

_____

2 Add different subordinate clauses in **different positions** in this sentence.

a Start: _____ , Ellie began to cry.

b Middle: Ellie, _____ , began to cry.

c End: Ellie began to cry _____ .

3 Reorder the clauses in these sentences to make them more effective.

a Mrs Atkins saw everything, looking out of her window.

_____

b The boy continued to watch cartoons, ignoring the fuss around him.

_____

c I always enjoy my uncle's visits although he is eccentric.

_____

For help with the questions on this page see
Understanding English: Grammar **pages 36–37 and 41.**

Grammar Different types of sentence

1 Write a **statement**, a **question**, a **command** and an **exclamation**, each with the word 'rubbish' in it.

a Statement: _____

b Question: _____

c Command: _____

d Exclamation: _____

2 Write **questions** to follow these statements and draw the reader in.

a There was a bridge across the river. _____

b The centre needs volunteers. _____

c It was a dead end. _____

d First prize is a luxury cruise. _____

3 Complete the following as **conditional** sentences.

a If I won the lottery _____ .

b I always do my homework _____ .

4 Rewrite these sentences in the **passive** form and hide who or what is doing the actions.

a The dog followed the man through the darkened streets.

_____

b Millie had eaten the last blueberry muffin.

_____

c We watered the plants every day.

_____

For help with the questions on this page see
Understanding English: Grammar **pages 38–39 and 48–51.**

1 Rewrite these sentences to make each event seem more likely.

a Isla might come. _____

b Maybe she can help. _____

2 Correct the **grammatical errors** in these sentences.

a There is piles of papers on them chairs so no-one has nowhere to sit.

b Sanjay's model were real good but Sam's was betterest.

c Dom and me found a egg what had a broken shell.

d The builder falled through an hole in me roof.

3 **a** Add a **question tag** to make this sentence into a question.

You will help _____

b Rewrite this sentence as a formal **request**.

Can you help me? _____

c Complete this sentence using the **subjunctive** form sometimes used in formal writing.

I wish I _____ able to help you, but sadly it is not possible.

4 Which of these sentences is the **impersonal** version? Tick one.

I am too busy to do everything. ☐

I don't have enough time to get things done. ☐

Sometimes there is not enough time to do everything. ☐

For help with the questions on this page see
Understanding English: Grammar pages 29–31, 46–47 and 53–55.

Punctuation **Full stops and capital letters**

1 Write these sentences using the correct **punctuation**.

   a the man was delighted _____

   b gemma wrote two postcards _____

   c the snake slithered free _____

   d a lizard is a reptile _____

   e they painted the sky blue _____

2 Read the following pieces of writing. Decide where the **full stops** and **capital letters** are needed and add them.

   a all birds have wings most birds use their wings to fly

   _____

   b wait for the milk to boil keep stirring all the time

   _____

   c the girl was not listening she was too busy reading harry potter

   _____

   d let me tell you about my holiday we went to spain

   _____

   e no-one was looking she took jo's pen from her pocket and scribbled something on the pad

   _____

3 Write a sentence with three capital letters and a full stop.

   _____

4 Write a sentence with four capital letters and a full stop.

   _____

5 Write a sentence with five capital letters and a full stop.

   _____

For help with the questions on this page see
Understanding English: Punctuation **pages 4–5 and 8.**

1 Read each sentence and decide if it should have a **full stop**, a **question mark** or an **exclamation mark**. Write it in the box.

a Is paper made from trees ☐

b What a star ☐

c Could Annie have been right ☐

d Run, run as fast as you can ☐

e There was silence in the hall ☐

f But what can we do about it ☐

2 Write a sentence using a **question mark** and the word 'monkey'.

_____

3 Write a sentence using an **exclamation mark** and the word 'monkey'.

_____

4 **Proofread** this piece of writing. Add the **sentence punctuation**.

an old man was sitting in his kitchen he was thinking about his supper would he have a bowl of hot soup or leftover fish stew the old man's stomach rumbled at the thought of food rat-a-tat-tat rat-a-tat-tat there was a sudden knocking at the door who could it be at this time the man was not expecting company he got up and hobbled over to the door he opened the door a crack and peered out then he stared in amazement on his doorstep stood the King the King in person

For help with the questions on this page see
Understanding English: Punctuation pages 6–7 and 9.

Punctuation Commas

1 Complete these sentences by adding a **list** of **five** items or examples.

a In the picnic basket they found _____

_____ .

b A glance around the storeroom revealed _____

_____ .

c For the camping trip, you will need _____

_____ .

d _____

are all types of big cat.

2 A **comma** is missing from each sentence. Write the sentences correctly.

a I'm waiting for an answer Tarik. _____

b Unfortunately it was too late. _____

c No we cannot do that. _____

d Mum was right as usual. _____

e You will come won't you? _____

f At that moment the door shut. _____

3 Put the missing **commas** in this text.

> Later that evening Gran unpacked her bag. She took out her knitting her library book her glasses and a pack of toffees. Carefully she placed each item on the table. Gran likes to have everything neat and tidy you see.

For help with the questions on this page see
Understanding English: Punctuation pages 10 and 18–19.

Punctuation Apostrophes

1 Write the shortened forms or **contractions** of these words and phrases.

a do not → _____   **f** we will → _____

b it is → _____   **g** they have → _____

c she is → _____   **h** have not → _____

d I would → _____   **i** you will → _____

e you are → _____   **j** will not → _____

2 Rewrite these phrases using just **three words** and an **apostrophe** for **possession**.

a the book belonging to my father → _____

b the faces of the children → _____

c the whistle belonging to the referee → _____

d the ship belonging to the pirates → _____

e the hats belonging to the clowns → _____

f the egg belonging to the dinosaur → _____

3 **Apostrophes** are missing from these sentences. Underline where they should go and write these words correctly.

a Amirs gone to Emmas house and Im stuck here. _____

b The sharks teeth were bigger than Dads hand. _____

c Ben says thats why he wont play in Kofis team. _____

d I wasnt surprised when the players heads dropped. _____

For help with the questions on this page see
***Understanding English: Punctuation* pages 11–13.**

Punctuation Inverted commas

1 Add the **words spoken** to complete these lines of **dialogue**.

a _____ demanded Mum.

b _____ said the lion to the mouse.

c _____ cried Marcus loudly.

d _____ ordered the police sergeant.

e _____ the monkey asked the hippo.

f The conductor yelled _____.

2 Change these examples of **reported speech** into **direct speech**. Don't use 'said' in your answers.

a He said he would meet me at one o'clock.

_____

b He asked her how she knew about the diamonds.

_____

c Rosie shouted for her to go back.

_____

d The man said he had not seen the red light because of the fog.

_____

3 Insert the correct punctuation into each sentence.

a The bank robber shouted Hand over the money

b Where are you called Meena I can't see you

For help with the questions on this page see
Understanding English: Punctuation pages 14–15 and *Understanding English: Grammar* page 52.

Practice

Punctuation Setting out direct speech

1 Rewrite this script as **direct speech** for a narrative text.

Jake: I'm bored

Dev *(with a sigh)*: I'm bored too.

Fatima: I'm so bored I'm bored with being bored.

Jake *(standing up)*: Well, let's do something then.

Dev: Like what?

Jake: We could go to the park.

_____

_____

_____

_____

_____

_____

2 **a** Read this **dialogue** shown in speech bubbles.

Grasshopper

Ant

Hey, slow down. Come and …

Sorry, I'm much too busy.

b What is the name of the punctuation mark at the end of the first speech bubble?

colon ☐   hyphen ☐   ellipsis ☐   dash ☐

c Explain why this punctuation mark is needed.

_____

d Write what the ant says as **direct speech** using inverted commas

_____

For help with the questions on this page see
Understanding English: Punctuation page 16 and *Understanding English: Grammar* page 52.

Punctuation Commas and subordinate clauses

1 Do these sentences need a **comma** or not? Write 'comma' or 'no comma'.

 a The school was closed because it had flooded. _____

 b Exhausted by the events he fell asleep. _____

 c She approached the wizard hoping to find the answer. _____

 d He whistled as he squelched through the grass. _____

 e Although the storm raged she was safe inside. _____

2 **Three** of the sentences above need a comma. Write them correctly.

_____

_____

_____

3 Complete these sentences so they start with a **subordinate clause**. Remember to use a **comma** to separate the clauses.

 a Because the dragon _____.

 b Even though the _____.

 c As it was nearly _____.

 d Surprised by _____.

 e Storming through _____.

4 Read these sentences and add the commas where needed.

 a Slowly he crept down the corridor. Holding the lamp high he felt along the wall.

 b Setting off once more the traveller quickened her pace. She knew that time was running out yet she was still far from home.

 c When the race began everyone set off enthusiastically. Full of energy they sprinted across the field.

 d The twins carried four plates each piled high with sandwiches.

For help with the questions on this page see
Understanding English: Punctuation pages 20–23.

Punctuation Comma or full stop?

1 Read the following. Have the **commas** been used correctly? Put a *tick* if the comma is correct. Put a *cross* if the comma should really be a **full stop**.

a It was time to leave, they put on their overcoats. ☐

b As I entered the password, the screen suddenly lit up. ☐

c Handing over the letters, she felt uneasy. ☐

d It was nearly noon, we were going to miss the train. ☐

e Samson's field is a special place, it must not be spoilt. ☐

f Before he could scream, someone grabbed him. ☐

2 **Three** of the sentences above were incorrect. Write them correctly.

_____

_____

_____

3 In the following texts, **commas** have sometimes been used when really there should be a **full stop**. Read the text and make the necessary corrections.

a It was a stormy day, the wind roared down the chimney, rain splattered the window.

b She watched, scared to move, she had never seen a motor car before, never even heard one.

c Frantically, she ran down the corridor, slipping and stumbling, she had to escape.

d After a long time, when the smoke finally cleared, Simon found himself standing on a cliff-top, he was quite alone, Marsha had vanished.

For help with the questions on this page see
Understanding English: Punctuation **page 24.**

Punctuation Commas, brackets and dashes

1 Use **two commas** to add **extra information** to each of these sentences.

   a Chioma _____ crossed the finishing line.

   b Mr Singh _____ was first on the scene.

   c The owl _____ watched them carefully.

   d Tess _____ was the first to volunteer.

2 Add **brackets** in the correct position in each of these sentences.

   a Fry the onions until soft two to three minutes before adding the herbs.

   b In the wardrobe he kept shoes red, silver and gold and matching hats.

   c You can feed birds with kitchen leftovers bread, cake, apple cores, bacon rind in the winter months.

   d Mrs Slater the head teacher spoke to Class 6.

3 Use a **dash** to add something surprising or dramatic to the **end** of these sentences.

   a Maybe they had been captured _____ .

   b Mia recognised the smell at once _____ .

   c I like the look of these young earthlings _____ .

   d The sack was stuffed with something _____ .

4 Use **two dashes** to add **extra information** to these sentences.

   a She let out a scream _____ and raced out of the room.

   b There was a spider _____ sitting in the bath.

   c Mr Green _____ is very stern.

   d It was cold _____ so we stayed inside.

For help with the questions on this page see
Understanding English: Punctuation **pages 26–29.**

Practice

1 Add a **colon** to the end of each sentence and then complete the sentence with some further information.

a He read the name on the envelope _____ .

b Bread has only four main ingredients _____ .

c I have just one motto in life _____ .

2 Rewrite each pair of sentences as one sentence. Use a **semicolon** rather than a conjunction.

a No-one else was in the room. I was quite alone.

_____

b The first book was good. The others were disappointing.

_____

c I did not go out. It was too cold.

_____

3 Add a colon or semicolon in the correct place in these sentences.

a This story has it all an exotic setting, a thrilling adventure and an unbelievable ending.

b Some people like city living others prefer life in the country.

4 There should be **three hyphens** in this sentence. Write it correctly.

A crowd was forming, with grown ups and children, wide eyed toddlers and curious passers by, all straining to see.

_____

_____

For help with the questions on this page see
Understanding English: Punctuation **pages 30–32 and 34–35.**

Vocabulary Word meanings

1 Read these sentences and write the **meaning** of the word in **bold**.

a Uniform is **compulsory** for all pupils.   _____

b He was alone on the **desolate** planet.   _____

c The wind **buffeted** the children.   _____

d Bravely, she **brandished** the sword.   _____

e The puzzle was **infuriatingly** difficult.   _____

f He must **dispel** any thoughts of home.   _____

2 Draw lines to match these words with their **definitions**.

permanent   the same in every detail

reinforced   not clear or transparent

identical   made stronger

opaque   fixed or lasting

3 Write a sentence using **two** of the words from question 2.

_____

4 Write a **definition** for each of these words.

a recline   _____

b contemplate _____

c anthology   _____

d conceal   _____

e sufficient   _____

f remote   _____

g modify   _____

For help with the questions on this page see
***Understanding English: Vocabulary* pages 4–6 and 14.**

Vocabulary Word roots

1 Write the **root word** for each of these words.

a pressure _____ **d** publication _____ **g** declassify _____

b enjoyment _____ **e** reaction _____ **h** significant _____

c description _____ **f** disobedient _____ **i** muscular _____

2 Write **four** words that come from the same **word family** as these root words.

a part _____ _____ _____ _____

b act _____ _____ _____ _____

3 Find and write **four** words that start with each of these familiar **prefixes**.

a aero air _____ _____ _____ _____

b aqua water _____ _____ _____ _____

c audi hear _____ _____ _____ _____

d tri three _____ _____ _____ _____

e super more than, beyond _____ _____ _____ _____

4 Underline the **common root** or **prefix** in each set of words. Write the **meaning** of that word part.

a submarine, submerge, subway _____

b transport, porter, export, portable _____

c exit, export, expel, exterior _____

d international, intercom, intervene _____

e bicycle, binoculars, bilingual _____

For help with the questions on this page see
Understanding English: Vocabulary pages 7–9.

Vocabulary Homographs

1 Which **homographs** have the following **two meanings**?

a the sound of a bell and a piece of jewellery _____

b not heavy and not dark _____

c to shape into something and a document to fill in _____

d to pull something sharply and a small boat _____

2 Write **two** different **meanings** for these homographs.

a pupil _____ _____

b watch _____ _____

c club _____ _____

3 Underline the **two homographs** in each of these lists of words.

a bat   lizard   crane   elephant

b pie   berry   pop   jam

c door   table   desk   book

4 Write sentences that show the different meanings of these homographs.

a stable (noun) _____

stable (adjective) _____

b rock (noun) _____ _____

rock (verb) _____

c mean (adjective) _____

mean (verb) _____

For help with the questions on this page see
Understanding English: Vocabulary **pages 12–13.**

Vocabulary Synonyms

1 Underline the **four synonyms** in each of these lists of words.

a easy   simple   empty   uncomplicated   clean   straightforward

b sprint   pour   gush   stream   jostle   spurt

c tidy   tight   neat   organised   drab   orderly

d pull   push   drag   haul   tug   drive

e solid   lean   hollow   slender   thin   slight

2 Write **three** or **four** synonyms that could be used in place of the word in **bold**.

a It was a **boring** event. _____

b The crowd were **excited**. _____

c It is **hot** here. _____

d The dish was **tasty**. _____

e It is **quiet** inside. _____

f He went for a **quick** run. _____

3 Rewrite the following text using synonyms to replace the word that is used too many times.

> With a hideous howl, the hideous creature rose out of the swamp. A hideous smell filled the air. I caught just a glimpse of its hideous features.

_____

_____

_____

For help with the questions on this page see
Understanding English: Vocabulary pages 18–20.

Vocabulary Choosing the best word

1   In the box are words you could use instead of the word 'jumps'. Choose the **best word** for each occasion. Don't use the same word twice.

    a   A jack-in-the-box **jumps** _____ up.

    b   The hero **jumps** _____ off.

    c   The gymnast **jumps** _____ over.

    d   The little green frog **jumps** _____ .

> vaults
> hops
> bounds
> leaps
> springs

2   In the box are words you might use instead of 'ate'. Choose the best word for each occasion. Don't use the same word twice.

    a   The Montagues **ate** _____ at seven thirty.

    b   The monster **ate** _____ its prey.

    c   The tortoise **ate** _____ its lettuce leaves.

    d   They **ate** _____ too much.

> consumed
> devoured
> chewed
> munched
> dined

3   In the box are words you might you use instead of 'big'. Choose the best word for each occasion. Don't use the same word twice.

    a   He was a **big** _____ star in the nineties.

    b   I saw **big** _____ skyscrapers.

    c   The site is **big** _____ .

    d   There was a **big** _____ explosion.

> vast
> gigantic
> colossal
> massive
> towering

4   Write a **synonym** that could be used for each of these.

    a   a little grumpy _____ → very grumpy _____

    b   a little frightened _____ → very frightened _____

For help with the questions on this page see
Understanding English: Vocabulary pages 16, 20 and 22–23.

Vocabulary Antonyms

1 Complete these pairs of **antonyms** or opposites.

a arrive _____

b weak _____

c stale _____

d friend _____

e absent _____

f curved _____

g imaginary _____

h question _____

i help _____

j guilty _____

2 Add a **prefix** to make the opposite of each word.

a _____do

b _____passable

c _____like

d _____fiction

e _____acceptable

f _____mature

g _____sensitive

h _____healthy

i _____active

j _____approve

k _____regular

l _____sufficient

m _____agree

n _____honest

o _____usual

3 Complete the **pairs** of antonyms in these sentences.

a Tom is the best runner and Harry is the _____ . Tom will win and

Harry will _____ .

b Some people are wise and others are _____ . Some people are right

and others are _____ .

c You have many talents and he has _____ . But he is hard-working

and you are _____ .

d This car is old and that one is _____ . This car is slow and that

one is _____ .

For help with the questions on this page see
Understanding English: Vocabulary **pages 8 and 21.**

Vocabulary Prefixes and suffixes

1 Add a **prefix** and **suffix** to each of these **root words** to make another word.

The first one has been done for you.

a <u>un</u> law <u>ful</u>

b ____employ____

c ____avoid____

d ____turn____

e ____willing____

f ____place____

g ____agree____

h ____manage____

i ____person____

j ____order____

k ____complete____

l ____help____

2 Add suffixes to these words to make them into **adjectives**.

a crisp_____

b bend_____

c pain_____

d peace_____

e break_____

f enjoy_____

g end_____

h spot_____

i tradition_____

j mass_____

k emotion_____

l taste_____

3 Suffixes have been removed from some words in these sentences. Add the suffixes needed for each sentence to make sense.

a The farm_____ was known throughout the king_____ for his fair_____, honest_____ and truth_____.

b The manage_____ said that hope_____ the team would be more success_____ next season and win the champion_____.

c The state_____ was critic_____ of the drive_____'s behaviour; it said the accident was entire_____ avoid_____.

d We use only the fresh_____ ingredients, season_____ vegetables and local_____ grown organ_____ produce.

For help with the questions on this page see
Understanding English: Vocabulary pages 8–11.

Vocabulary Old and new words

1 Read this text. Underline the **old, unfamiliar** words that are not used much today.

> He espied a purse of doubloons on the settle where the old gentleman in the red frockcoat had been seated.

2 Read this text. Underline the words that show this is a **more recent** text than the one above.

> A multimedia player allows you to stream audio and video files from the same interface. Free downloads available online.

3 Look closely at this list of words that have been recently **added** to the language.

tweet	sitcom	carjacking	tablet	wicked	spam
dancercise	text	wireless	fantabulous	camcorder	brunch

Sort the words to show how they came about.

Old words with a new meaning	Words formed from two existing words

4 Some words are 'borrowed' from other languages. Read each set of words below. Underline the words that you think come from another language.

a rugby   judo   skiing   football   badminton   sumo

b pizza   pancake   pie   chapatti   sandwich   coleslaw

c rat   dog   emu   gnu   goat   tarantula

d sock   kimono   hat   waistcoat   dungarees   sombrero

For help with the questions on this page see
Understanding English: Vocabulary **pages 28–33.**

Vocabulary New words and onomatopoeia

1 There are two **shortened forms** of words used in each of these phrases. Underline them and write them in their **full forms**.

a celebs and VIPs only _____ _____

b the DJ's limo _____ _____

c download apps and e-books _____ _____

d CCTV on Park Ave _____ _____

2 Add an appropriate **onomatopoeic** word and **punctuation** mark to go before each of these sentences.

a _____ The cake landed on the floor.

b _____ There was glass everywhere.

c _____ The door slowly opened.

d _____ Off flew the broomstick.

3 Write down **four** onomatopoeic words to use when describing rain falling on an umbrella.

_____

4 Write **definitions** for these **recently invented** words.

a staycation _____

b travelator _____

c spellathon _____

d guesstimate _____

e chillax _____

f cybercrime _____

For help with the questions on this page see
Understanding English: Vocabulary **pages 30–31 and 36.**

Vocabulary Formal and informal words

1 You are writing about a new idea or invention. Look at the words below. Which would you use in a **personal diary** and which would you use in a **formal letter**?

brainwave	concept	gizmo	device	my associate
ingenious	nifty	complication	snag	my mate

Words to use in a personal diary	Words to use in a formal letter

2 Write **three** words that are more **formal** to use in place of these words.

a to throw away → _____ _____ _____

b to tell (someone) → _____ _____ _____

c to get → _____ _____ _____

d horrible → _____ _____ _____

e fussy → _____ _____ _____

3 Rewrite these sentences using more formal words.

a It was a posh do. _____

b I didn't get it. _____

c The business went bust. _____

d He had to come clean. _____

For help with the questions on this page see
***Understanding English: Vocabulary* pages 26–27.**

Spelling Tricky letter strings

1 Write in the **letter string** that is missing from each *set* of words.

a h __ __ __ d   s __ __ __ ch   l __ __ __ n   __ __ __ th

b trea __ __ __ __   plea __ __ __ __   lei __ __ __ __   mea __ __ __ __

c flav __ __ __   rum __ __ __   col __ __ __   fav __ __ __ ite

d spec __ __ __   soc __ __ __   offic __ __ __   artific __ __ __

e p __ __ __ e   c __ __ __ e   bec __ __ __ e   appl __ __ __ e

2 Write the **past tense** of these verbs.

a think _____   **c** bring _____

b buy _____   **d** fight _____

3 Write **three** more words with the same **letter pattern**.

a world   worship   _____   _____   _____

b eight   height   _____   _____   _____

4 Underline the words below that are **wrongly spelt**. Write them correctly.

a I wud if I cud. _____

b I was not tuff enuff. _____

c We fownd it on the grownd. _____

d Put the notise in the offise. _____   _____

e I am shure that my friend was nervus. _____

f Peeple once beleived the Earth to be flat. _____

g The fewcha of the stashun looks bright. _____

For help with the questions on this page see
Understanding English: Spelling pages 10 and 12.

Practice

Spelling Tricky letters

1 Choose the **correct spelling** for the missing **sound** in these words. Write it in.

a stoma_____   ch ck

b s_____mbol   i y

c _____antom   f ph

d gu_____de   i y

e gra_____   ff ph

f ma_____ine   sh ch

g e_____o   ch ck

h s_____stem   i y

i _____ef   sh ch

j rh_____me   i y

k _____rase   f ph

l ya_____t   ch ck

2 Underline the **misspelt word** in each sentence. Write the word correctly.

a Lemons are biter.   _____

b The children had super.   _____

c I can use comas.   _____

3 All these words are spelt wrongly. Write each word correctly.

a ritten   _____

b num   _____

c nash   _____

d neel   _____

e wisper   _____

f casle   _____

g climeing _____

h restling   _____

i dout   _____

j riggle   _____

4 Underline the words below that are **incorrect**. Write them correctly.

a A strange voise cut through the silense.   _____

b Resently the city had exsiting news.   _____

c In the sentre was a large, rijid structure.   _____

d It was a chanje for Andy to say something intellijent.   _____

For help with the questions on this page see
Understanding English: Spelling **pages 13–15.**

Spelling Syllables and compound words

1 Look at these words. Circle the **compound words**.

teapot	uphill	cotton	mascot	popcorn
forest	visit	dustbin	desktop	offer

2 A part of these compound words is **spelt wrongly**. Write each compound word correctly in its two parts.

a tracksoot = _____ + _____

b clokeroom = _____ + _____

c warterfall = _____ + _____

d harf-time = _____ + _____

e warkway = _____ + _____

f hartburn = _____ + _____

g cowntdown = _____ + _____

h cupbord = _____ + _____

i moterbike = _____ + _____

j quorterback = _____ + _____

3 Write **four** compound words that include the word 'body'.

_____   _____   _____   _____

4 Count the **syllables** in each of these words. Write the number in the box.

a trumpet ☐

b holiday ☐

c calendar ☐

d helicopter ☐

e shampoo ☐

f family ☐

g brilliant ☐

h extraordinary ☐

i combination ☐

j hotel ☐

k important ☐

l activity ☐

5 Add the missing syllable(s) into each of these words. (**Clue:** they are all animals.)

a chim / _____ / zee

b cat / _____ / _____ / lar

c fla / _____ / go

d kan / _____ / roo

e al / _____ / _____ / tor

f but / _____ / fly

g pel / _____ / can

h buf / _____ / lo

i sal / _____ / _____ / der

For help with the questions on this page see
Understanding English: Spelling **pages 4–6.**

Spelling Adding prefixes and suffixes

1 These words all have **prefixes**. Put a *tick* if the word is spelt correctly; put a *cross* if it is wrong.

a allways ☐   d mislay ☐   g antefreeze ☐

b almost ☐   e dissappear ☐   h illegal ☐

c misspell ☐   f imature ☐   i nonesense ☐

2 **Five** of the words had **incorrect spellings**. Write them correctly.

_____   _____   _____

_____   _____

3 Add the three **suffixes** to each of the **root words**.

a smoke er less y   _____   _____   _____

b tune ful less er   _____   _____   _____

c like ly ness en   _____   _____   _____

d lone ly er some   _____   _____   _____

4 Complete these word sums.

a plenty + ful = _____   g happy + ly = _____

b beauty + ful = _____   h hungry + ly = _____

c fancy + ful = _____   i rely + able = _____

d joy + ful = _____   j enjoy + able = _____

e happy + ness = _____   k vary + ous = _____

f laze + ness = _____   l history + ic = _____

For help with the questions on this page see
Understanding English: Spelling pages 26–31.

Spelling Unstressed vowels

1 Add the missing **vowel** to each of these words.

a math___matics   **e** popul__r   **i** gen___ral

b libr__ry   **f** hospit__l   **j** sev__ral

c hist__ry   **g** gramm__r   **k** sim__lar

d Janu__ry   **h** mis__rable   **l** sep__rate

2 Add the missing **syllable** to each of these words.

a mar __ __ __ lous   (wonderful or amazing)

b Feb __ __ ary   (the second month of the year)

c dif __ __ rent   (not the same)

d cor __ __ dor   (passageway in a building)

e deaf __ __ ing   (very loud)

3 One word in each sentence is **spelt wrongly**. Underline it. Write it correctly.

a It was a frightning experience. _____

b He made a genrous donation to charity. _____

c I will proburbly grab a sandwich for lunch. _____

d They are offring to buy the company. _____

e I was desprate to escape. _____

f All my family are intrested in animals. _____

4 Underline the **unstressed vowel** in each of these words.

important   definite   average   ordinary   sentence

For help with the questions on this page see
Understanding English: Spelling **page 17.**

Practice

Spelling Homophones

1 Complete these pairs of **homophones**.

a flower and _____

b steal and _____

c guest and _____

d right and _____

e seen and _____

f who's and _____

g not and _____

h main and _____

i key and _____

j cereal and _____

2 Each sentence contains **two** homophone **errors**. Underline the errors and write those words correctly.

a It was as plane as the knows on my face. _____ _____

b The bare in the zoo looked board. _____ _____

c Water was leeking from a whole. _____ _____

d Brake off a peace of bread. _____ _____

e I new it would be a grate event. _____ _____

3 Write a sentence containing **both** the given homophones. Make sure the word **meanings** are clear.

a ate and eight _____

b threw and through _____

c heard and herd _____

d aloud and allowed _____

4 Underline the errors in this sentence and write the words correctly.

Their were two many stars too count. _____

For help with the questions on this page see
Understanding English: Spelling **pages 18–19.**

1 Write the correct spelling of each of these **plurals**.

a glassis _____

b groupes _____

c chorusis _____

d heartes _____

e gooses _____

f touchs _____

g bruisis _____

h echos _____

i answeres _____

j womans _____

2 Change these words to plurals.

a one country, two _____

b one copy, two _____

c one story, two _____

d one puppy, two _____

e one journey, two _____

f one reply, two _____

g one buggy, two _____

h one trolley, two _____

i one donkey, two _____

j one city, two _____

k one lorry, two _____

l one army, two _____

3 Rewrite these sentences with **plural nouns**.

a The ~~elf~~ danced along the ~~shelf~~. _____

b The ~~wife~~ took the ~~calf~~ to market. _____

c The ~~thief~~ wore a ~~scarf~~. _____

4 Add the correct **plural ending** to the nouns in this list. Modify the noun ending where needed.

For my birthday I had ten balloon_____, nine ice lolly_____, eight fruit loaf_____,

seven badge_____, six teddy_____, five pair_____ of shoe_____, four magic fish_____,

three money box_____, two gold watch_____ and one bag of ruby_____.

For help with the questions on this page see
Understanding English: Spelling pages 20–21.

Spelling Adding –ed and –ing

1 Add **–ing** to the end of each of these **verbs**. Modify the verb ending where needed.

a build_____   f create_____   k scatter_____

b surprise_____   g admit_____   l enjoy_____

c hug_____   h suggest_____   m welcome_____

d carry_____   i win_____   n consider_____

e plan_____   j write_____   o propel_____

2 Complete this table. Write in the **past tense form** of each of the verbs.

Present	Past	Present	Past
impress		regret	
stop		divide	
decide		obey	
reply		carry	
admit		glance	
scamper		frighten	
command		topple	
study		equip	

3 Add **–ed** and **–ing** endings to the verbs in these sentences so that they make sense.

a Leave_____ the trolley, the woman grab_____ her shop_____ and dash_____ out of

the supermarket.

b Startle_____ by the sudden boom, Amit drop_____ to the ground, his heart race_____ .

c The creatures hurry_____ and scurry_____ here and there, explore_____ every surface

and search_____ in every hole.

For help with the questions on this page see
Understanding English: Spelling **pages 22–24.**

Spelling Tricky word endings 1

1 Underline the word that is **spelt wrongly** in each sentence. Write it correctly.

a It was an unpleasant sensashun.

b It was a special occashun.

c A feroshous roar soon had our attention.

d Offishal figures show the population is growing.

e The caushus driver went in the wrong direction.

f A big attraction is essenshal.

g Did I mension the delicious meal?

2 Add the correct 'shun' **ending** to change each of these words into a **noun**. Write the noun.

a reduce

b create

c exclude

d persuade

e construct

f distract

g discuss

h progress

i extend

j conclude

k produce

l infect

m explode

n possess

3 Add the missing syllables. Use the clues to help you.

a de / _____ / _____ / _____   (**Clue:** the meaning of a word)

b com / _____ / _____ / _____   (**Clue:** a contest to find the winner)

c punc / _____ / _____ / _____   (**Clue:** marks such as full stops and commas)

d in / _____ / _____ / _____   (**Clue:** data)

For help with the questions on this page see
Understanding English: Spelling **pages 34 and 36.**

Spelling Tricky word endings 2

1 These words all end with **–able** or **–ible**. Write each word with the **correct ending**.

a avoid _____

b imposs _____

c remark _____

d terr _____

e change _____

f value _____

g ed _____

h predict _____

i avail _____

j invis _____

k horr _____

l regret _____

m accept _____

n reason _____

2 Underline the **correct spelling** of the two choices given.

a A **trickle trickel** of water! Now we are in **trouble troubel**!

b I wrote a **lable label** to go on the **model modal** ship.

c Lighting **candles candels** made the scene **magicle magical**.

d He was **hesitant hesitent** and **reluctant reluctent** at the beginning.

e The pen was in the **originol original** **metal metel** case.

f **Apparantly Apparently** she is a **frequant frequent** visitor.

3 Underline the **two misspelt words** in each sentence. Write them correctly.

a I recieved a brief note from my nieghbour. _____ _____

b A feirce blow pierced the sheild. _____ _____

c I beleive my freind may have been deceitful. _____ _____

d The thief shreiked as he fell through the cieling. _____ _____

e Each peice of news brought grief or releif. _____ _____

For help with the questions on this page see
Understanding English: Spelling pages 11, 16 and 35.

Schofield & Sims | Understanding English

45

Fiction Character clues

In the **novel** *Treasure Island*, young Jim Hawkins helps his parents to run the Admiral Benbow Inn.
Read the extracts and the questions beneath them. Early in the story, a stranger arrives …

Treasure Island

He was a pale, tallowy creature, wanting two fingers of the left hand; and though he
wore a cutlass, he did not look much like a fighter … He was not sailorly, and yet he had
a smack of the sea about him …

> **tallow** animal fat used in candles
> **cutlass** curved short sword
> **smack** hint, suggestion

Write your answers on a separate sheet of paper.

1 Underline the phrases that tell us what the stranger **looks like**.

2 What are your **first impressions** of the stranger? Explain your answer.

Now read this **dialogue** between young Jim and the stranger.

> … he motioned me to draw near. I paused where I was with my napkin in my hand.
> 'Come here, sonny,' says he. 'Come nearer here.' I took a step nearer.
> 'Is this here table for my mate Bill?' he asked, with a kind of leer.
> I told him I did not know his mate Bill; and this was for a person who stayed in our house
> whom we called the captain.

3 Does Jim **trust** the stranger? Give a reason for your answer.

4 In the dialogue, does the stranger sound **friendly**? Explain your answer.

Read more about the stranger's **behaviour**.

> The stranger kept hanging about just outside the inn door, peering round the corner like
> a cat waiting for a mouse. Once I stepped out myself into the road, but he immediately
> called me back, and, as I did not obey quick enough for his fancy, a most horrible change
> came over his tallowy face, and he ordered me in, with an oath that made me jump.
>
> Adapted from **Treasure Island**
> by **Robert Louis Stevenson** (1850–1894)

5 What does the stranger's behaviour tell us about him and why he has come to the inn?

For help with the questions on this page see
Understanding English: Fiction pages 4–6 and 15.

Fiction Creating characters

Imagine you are **writing a story** that starts with the **arrival of a stranger** at your home or school.

1 Write **two sentences** describing the stranger's **appearance**. Make the stranger sound **pleasant**.

_____

_____

2 Now write **two** sentences making the stranger sound **unpleasant** or threatening.

_____

_____

3 Write a short exchange of **dialogue** that makes the stranger sound warm and **friendly**.

_____

_____

_____

4 Now write an exchange of dialogue that makes the character seem **unfriendly** or untrustworthy.

_____

_____

_____

5 Choose _either_ the warm friendly character _or_ the unfriendly character. Write a short **paragraph** describing the character's **actions** and **behaviour**.

_____

_____

_____

_____

For help with the questions on this page see
Understanding English: Fiction **pages 7 and 16.**

Fiction Settings

In *Treasure Island,* Jim finds a pirate's map and sails to an island where the treasure is hidden. Read these extracts and the questions below. The extracts begin with Jim's first view of the island.

> Grey-coloured woods covered a large part of the surface. This even tint was indeed broken up by streaks of yellow sandbreak in the lower lands, and by many tall trees of the pine family, out-topping the others – some singly, some in clumps; but still the general colouring was uniform and sad.
>
> From **Treasure Island**
> by **Robert Louis Stevenson** *(1850–1894)*

Write your answers on a separate sheet of paper.

1 Does the island sound like a **pleasant** place? Explain your answer.

2 Find and copy **two** phrases that help to **create** this impression.

Here is a description of more sights and sounds of the island:

> … the island with its grey, melancholy woods, and wild stone spires, and the surf that we could both see and hear foaming and thundering on the steep beach …

3 How does this make you **feel** about the island?

4 Find and copy **three** phrases that create this effect.

5 Imagine you want to make the island sound **beautiful** and **welcoming**. Picture this new island. Add **details** below to create this new effect.

Parts of the island were _____ .

To the east _____ .

To the west _____ .

At the island's edge _____ .

Around the island _____ .

For help with the questions on this page see
Understanding English: Fiction pages 8–11.

Fiction Different points of view

Reread the second extract from *Treasure Island* on page 46 and think about **who** is telling the story. Then answer these questions about the point of view in *Treasure Island*.

1 From what **point of view** is the story told?

_____

2 What are the **clues** that tell you this?

_____

_____

_____

3 Why do you think the author chose to tell the story from this point of view?

_____

_____

_____

4 What do you learn about the storyteller's **feelings**? Write your answer in the thought bubble.

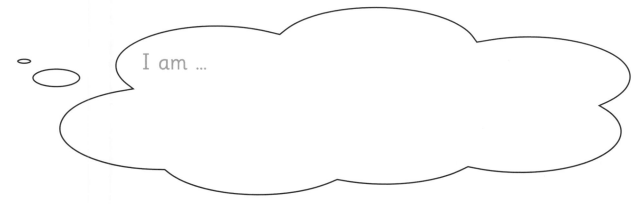

I am …

5 The events described on page 46 might look **different** if they were written from the stranger's point of view. Write about the arrival at the inn from this point of view.

_____

_____

_____

_____

For help with the questions on this page see
***Understanding English: Fiction* pages 12–13.**

Fiction Creating effects

Read this extract from *Treasure Island* where Jim and his mother are secretly searching through the captain's sea chest.

> I suddenly put my hand upon her arm; for I had heard in the silent, frosty air a sound that brought my heart into my mouth – the tap-tapping of the blind man's stick upon the frozen road. It drew nearer and nearer, while we sat holding our breath. Then it struck sharp on the inn door, and then we could hear the handle being turned, and the bolt rattling as the wretched being tried to enter; and then there was a long time of silence both within and without ...
>
> From **Treasure Island**
> by **Robert Louis Stevenson** (1850–1894)

1 How does this extract make you **feel**? Give a reason for your response.

_____ .

2 What was the writer's main **purpose** in writing this paragraph? Tick one.

a to develop character ☐   **c** to describe the setting ☐

b to build suspense and tension ☐   **d** to give a message or theme ☐

3 Explain **how** the author has created this effect:

a in the choice of words → _____

_____

b in the way the event is described → _____

_____

4 Use similar **techniques** to continue this story extract effectively.

It was dark in the tunnel – but there was something up ahead.

_____

_____

_____

For help with the questions on this page see
Understanding English: Fiction pages 30–35.

Fiction Plotting the main events

Here are the main events in the story *Treasure Island* but they are listed in the wrong order.

- Jim discovers the ship's crew are pirates, who also want the treasure.
- Jim finds a treasure map in an old sailor's sea chest.
- Jim returns home safely with his share of the treasure.
- Jim and his allies have a long battle with the pirates.
- Jim sets sail to find the island where the treasure is hidden.
- Jim, with help from his friends, outwits the pirates and locates the treasure.

1 Complete this flow chart to plot the events listed above in the correct order. You don't need to know the whole story – you should be able to work it out

The event that starts the story off:

↓

As a result ...

↓

However, there is a problem/complication:

↓

So ...

↓

Luckily the problem is resolved:

↓

So in the end ...

For help with the questions on this page see
Understanding English: Fiction page 21.

Read this **story** then answer the questions.

The Golden Touch

There was once a King named Midas who loved gold. One day King Midas was granted a wish by the god Dionysus. 'I wish that everything I touch shall turn to gold,' said the King gleefully.

'Are you sure?' asked the god with a frown. The King was quite sure. In fact, he insisted that his wish was granted immediately. And it was …

The King was thrilled. He rushed around touching all sorts of things. Cups and cabinets, books and barrels, helmets and horses – all turned to solid gold. But by lunchtime, the King was hungry. He picked up some bread – it turned to gold in his hand! He tried an apple … some water … but they also turned to gold. 'What will happen to me?' moaned the King. 'Perhaps this wasn't a good idea!'

The King's daughter came to comfort him, but she too turned to gold. The king was distraught. 'Whatever shall I do?' he wept.

Finally, the god Dionysus took pity on King Midas and sent him to the river to wash away the golden touch. His daughter and all the other golden items were restored to their normal state – much to the King's relief.

1 Write **two** words to describe the **character** of King Midas at the start of the story. Give reasons for your choices.

a _____ because _____

b _____ because _____

2 What is the **message** of the story?

_____

_____

3 What **traditional story features** did you notice? Give examples.

a characters _____

b setting _____

c events _____

d themes _____

> **For help with the questions on this page see**
> *Understanding English: Fiction pages 18–20.*

Fiction Plotting and retelling a story

1 Think about the story 'The Golden Touch'. Explain how this is the **turning point** in the story: 'He picked up some bread – it turned to gold in his hand!'.

_____

_____

_____

2 Plan your own story based on 'The Golden Touch' and its turning point. Plot the **main events** in this flow chart.

Who is the story about? What is he/she like?

↓

A wish is granted ...

↓

What happens?

↓

But then the turning point:

↓

What happens now?

↓

In the end ...

For help with the questions on this page see
Understanding English: Fiction pages 22–25 and 28–29.

Fiction Genre 1

Read each of these **three story openings**. Think about the **genre** of each story. Record your ideas about genre and **predict** what might happen in the story using your knowledge of the genre.

> **Story opening 1:** There was once a rather vain blackbird. This blackbird thought her feathers much glossier than those of other blackbirds, her beak more golden, her wings finer by far. The other blackbirds called her conceited but the vain blackbird didn't care what they thought.

1 Genre: _____

Recognisable features: _____

Prediction: _____

> **Story opening 2:** Whenever we stayed with Gran, she told us stories about a chilling sound heard on the moors on foggy nights. She said it was a wailing, or perhaps a moan. But whatever it was, no-one went out on the moors if a fog descended.

2 Genre: _____

Recognisable features: _____

Prediction: _____

> **Story opening 3:** Emerald stolen! So the headlines shouted as the story hit the front page. The police were following a number of leads but with little progress. Sam Hathaway took out his notebook, turned to a new page and made some notes.

3 Genre: _____

Recognisable features: _____

Prediction: _____

For help with the questions on this page see
Understanding English: Fiction pages 22–23 and 36–37.

Practice

Fiction Genre 2

This is a **summary** of the story *Treasure Island*.

> Jim discovers a treasure map. He sets off on a ship, across the oceans to the island where the treasure is hidden. There he must overcome many dangers and outwit the villainous Long John Silver and his crew of pirates. Only then can he return home safely with the treasure.

1   **a**   What **genre** of story is this? Tick one.

traditional tale ☐   ghost story ☐

science fiction ☐   realistic school story ☐

adventure ☐   detective mystery story ☐

b   Give reasons for your answer.

_____

_____

_____

2   Now try **changing the genre**: change details about the **characters**, **setting** and **events** so that the story sounds like a **science fiction** story.

Space commander Jim Hawkins discovers a _____ .

He sets off _____ .

There he must outwit _____ .

Only then can he _____ .

3   Now try changing the details again so that the story sounds like another genre.

_____

_____

_____

For help with the questions on this page see
Understanding English: Fiction pages 36–37 and 39.

Schofield & Sims I Understanding English

55

Read this **report** about traditional playground games.

Traditional playground games

Traditional playground games have existed for hundreds of years. They have been handed down through generations as younger children learn them from older brothers and sisters.

Skipping games

There are skipping games for individuals or pairs using a short rope, and games for large groups using a longer rope. Solo skippers or pairs count the number of skips, or perform tricks such as **Double Dutch**, **Can-can** and **Double skipping**. Often the jumping is accompanied by rhymes or songs.

Large group skipping games with a long rope require two turners. Any number of skippers can take it in turns to enter, jump the rope or perform another action, and then exit. Examples are **Under the moon and over the stars** and **Criss cross**.

Chasing games

These games involve a chaser running after the other players. The big advantage of chasing games is that no equipment is needed – just a lot of space. A simple example is **It**, also known as **Tig**, **Tag** or **Touch**. Once a player is touched by the chaser ('It'), then he or she becomes the chaser. Other examples of chasing games are **What's the time, Mr Wolf?** and **Stuck in the mud**.

Ball games

Ball-bouncing games need a small ball and are usually played singly. The ball is thrown against the wall and then caught. There are many variations such as **Dropsies** (letting the ball drop first) and **Clapsies** (clapping the hands before catching). **Piggy in the middle** is a ball game for at least three children, two throwing the ball to each other and one in the middle trying to catch it.

Other ball games involve two teams. The teams usually agree on an area of play and mark this with items such as jumpers. Examples are **Dodgeball**, which requires a large, light ball, and **Big side**.

1 What is the main **purpose** of this article?

_____

_____

1 The author of the text on page 56 tells us about a lot of different playground games. How has this information been **organised**?

_____

_____

2 Why are some words in the report in **bold** print?

_____

3 Complete this table to **summarise** the **key information** in the report.

Type of activity	Equipment needed	Example games
Skipping games		
Chasing games		

4 Match the following games with the correct **descriptions**.

Piggy in the middle   needs a marked area of play

Criss cross   a ball game for at least three children

Dodgeball   a skipping game requiring two turners

5 How did the **layout** and **presentation** of the report help you answer questions 3 and 4?

_____

_____

For help with the questions on these pages see
Understanding English: Non-fiction pages 8–10.

Non-fiction Organising ideas

Imagine you are **writing a report** on the **playground games** that are played at your school. Think about what you would include in your report.

1 Make notes below to show how you would **organise** your ideas.

Main heading

Subheading	Subheading

Subheading	Subheading

2 Think about how you would **start** your report. Write a short **introduction** for your report (**two sentences**).

_____

_____

_____

3 Write the **first sentence** for one **section** of your report.

Subheading: _____

First sentence: _____

_____

For help with the questions on this page see
Understanding English: Non-fiction **page 11.**

Read these **instructions** for downloading an imaginary game.

How to download a Planet Zukantta Adventure Game

- Click on the '**Planet Zukantta** Download' link. A download window will appear.

- Click 'Save' to save the game installer file to your computer.
  The download may take 5 or 10 minutes, so be patient.

- When the download is complete, the game installer icon will appear on the desktop.

- Double-click on the Installer to install the game. The Installer will take you through the few simple steps required to install the game.
  Important: You must accept the Licence Agreement when it appears or you will not be able to install the game.

Once the game is installed, you will find the **Planet Zukantta** game icon on your desktop. Double-click on the icon to begin your exciting adventures!

1 Do you think these instructions would be **easy to follow**? Give a reason for your answer.

_____

2 Why has the writer included the two sentences in *italics*?

_____

_____

3 Would these instructions be suitable for an **inexperienced** computer user? Give reasons for your answer.

_____

_____

4 How are these instructions **similar** to or **different** from a **recipe**?

Similar: _____

Different: _____

For help with the questions on this page see
Understanding English: Non-fiction pages 12–14.

Non-fiction Reading accounts

Read this extract from an **account** of a football match.

> What a day! What a match! What a winner! I can't believe it but we are through to the Cup Final. It has been an amazing day – although it didn't start off so well.
>
> When I went to pack my kit I couldn't find my lucky socks. They were in the wash. I had a huge argument with Mum about whether I could wear dirty socks for a Cup semi-final.
>
> In the end it was all sorted but we were really late leaving. We finally set off for the ground at 10 o'clock (half an hour later than planned) – only to discover within minutes that all the roads were blocked because of a burst water pipe. We just didn't move for half an hour.
>
> Finally, we reached the ground 10 minutes before kick-off time (11.00), to find we still only had nine players. The others were stuck in traffic as well. Eventually, Rick and Dipak turned up with minutes to spare, so at least we had a team. But Smithy still hadn't made it.
>
> The first half was a disaster. We were all over the place. Luckily, they weren't much better. But then their centre forward whacked one which swerved rather fortunately for them and we were 1-0 down.

1 a Is this a **personal** account or a **factual** account? _____

b What are the **clues** in the text that tell you this?

_____

_____

2 The writer says the day 'didn't start off so well'. What was the **first thing** that went wrong?

_____

3 Make a **timeline** to show the events in the hour leading up to kick-off.

10.00   11.00

For help with the questions on this page see
Understanding English: Non-fiction pages 16–18 and 20.

Read this **newspaper report**.

Cup Thriller

Falcons 3–2 Wanderers
(Smith 65, 90, Elliott 78; Keita 27, Brown 42)

Falcons are through to the final of the Junior Cup after a thrilling last-minute winner saw them overcome their local rivals on Saturday.

After a quiet opening with neither team showing any real fluency, Wanderers took the lead in the 27th minute when Keita blazed a shot that swerved into the top left-hand corner.

Just before half-time, Wanderers doubled their lead when Brown found the bottom corner after a goalmouth scramble.

At half-time both teams made substitutions with Falcons bringing on Smith and Wanderers bringing on Reeve to replace the injured Keita.

After the break, Falcons were much improved and began to pose more threat with some patient build-up play. This was rewarded with a goal in the 65th minute. A neat cross fell to Smith whose shot kept low, beating the Wanderer's goalkeeper.

Now the tempo of the match seemed to change completely as Falcons pressed forward for the equaliser.

(Report continued inside)

1 Use **clues** from the text to **predict** what happened next and how the match ended.

_____

_____

2 Why did the writer begin with the **headline** 'Cup Thriller'?

_____

_____

3 The texts on pages 60 and 61 describe the same event. How is this newspaper sports report **different** from the account on page 60?

_____

_____

_____

For help with the questions on this page see
***Understanding English: Non-fiction* pages 21–24.**

Non-fiction Writing accounts

1 Continue the **newspaper report** shown on page 61. Think about how to keep the report interesting and convincing. Use an appropriate style and voice.

_____

_____

_____

_____

_____

_____

2 Write the rest of the **personal account** begun on page 60. Remember to add personal **details** to bring the events to life, continuing in the same style.

_____

_____

_____

_____

_____

_____

3 Imagine you are a member of the losing side in the match. Write the **opening** for a personal account written from this **point of view**. Think about how to show the different reaction to the events.

_____

_____

_____

_____

For help with the questions on this page see
Understanding English: Non-fiction **pages 19 and 24–25.**

Read this **information**. Then answer the questions to check you understand.

What happens when you exercise?

Run around the playground, do 20 star jumps … What do you notice? What happens to your body?

1 When you start to move, your muscles have to work harder. They need more oxygen to keep going.

3 Your heart starts to beat more quickly. It is pumping blood around your body.

4 The blood is taking oxygen around your body – especially to those muscles.

2 You start to breathe more quickly. Your lungs are now working harder to get more oxygen into your body.

5 You start to feel hot. To help you cool down your body starts to sweat.

1 Explain why you breathe more quickly when exercising.

_____

2 Explain how blood is moved round your body.

_____

3 Explain why you sweat when you are exercising hard.

_____

4 Why do you think the author chose to **present** the information like this?

_____

_____

5 Why has the writer **numbered** the text boxes around the picture?

_____

For help with the questions on this page see
***Understanding English: Non-fiction* pages 34–36.**

Read this **advertisement** for an imaginary computer game.

Planet Zukantta – The greatest adventure game yet!

Can you save the planet?

Choose your character, master the skills, explore the amazing interactive world and embark on an action-packed adventure in spectacular 3D – you'll believe you're really there!

The clock is already ticking – get playing!

Parents
This game requires thinking skills, problem-solving and decision-making.

1 Find and copy **two claims** made in the main advert that are opinions rather than facts.

_____

_____

2 Find and copy **three** examples of persuasive **adjectives** or **noun phrases**.

_____

3 Why did the writer include the section headed 'Parents'?

_____

_____

_____

4 What other **techniques** have been used to capture the reader's interest? Give an example to support each answer.

_____

_____

_____

For help with the questions on this page see
Understanding English: Non-fiction pages 26–28.

Read this introduction to an **article**. Think about the issue. Then answer the questions.

Playtime games *versus* video games

Today is the age of the electronic game. Children are turning their backs on traditional playground or street games and embracing the hi-tech world of video and computer games. The many critics of these on-screen games say that they are anti-social time-wasters that damage the brain and body. Other people believe that video games can help train the brain and that children must move with the times. So what is the truth? What are the facts behind both arguments?

1 **a** What do you think is the writer's **opinion** on video games? Tick one.

Video games are bad. ☐   Video games are good. ☐   You cannot tell. ☐

b Give reasons for your answer.

_____

_____

_____

2 The introduction mentions points **for** and **against** video games. What are these?

a Points for: _____

_____

b Points against: _____

_____

3 Explain how the writer might **use** these two pieces of **information** in the rest of the article. Write your answers in the boxes.

a Scientists have found that video games help develop high-level thinking skills.	**b** Health experts recommend that children should enjoy an hour of physical activity each day.

For help with the questions on this page see
***Understanding English: Non-fiction* pages 30–32.**

Poetry Rhyme

1   Underline the words that **rhyme** in this poem.

Night lights
There is no need to light a night-light
On a light night like tonight
For a night-light's light is a slight light
When the moonlight's white and bright.
Anon

2   Describe the rhyme **pattern** in this poem. Write your ideas in the box.

From **The Months**
January cold desolate;
February all dripping wet;
March wind ranges;
April changes;
Birds sing in tune
To flowers of May;
And sunny June
Brings longest day.
by **Christina Rossetti**
(1830–1894)

3   Add the missing words to complete the **rhyming couplets**.

One times two makes two;   Two times two makes four;
Sunflowers as tall as _____ .   Red roses round the _____ .

4   Add **two lines** to complete this poem and make it rhyme.

Bridge across the river wide

_____

Beneath your arch the waters flow

_____

For help with the questions on this page see
Understanding English: Poetry pages 4–5 and 10.

Poetry Rhythm and reading aloud

1 Read aloud this extract from a long poem called 'The Pied Piper of Hamelin'. In this part of the poem, the piper begins to play and the children of Hamelin follow him. Think about the **sound** of the poem and the **effect** created.

Extract from **The Pied Piper of Hamelin**

There was a rustling, that seemed like a bustling
Of merry crowds justling at pitching and hustling,
Small feet were pattering, wooden shoes clattering,
Little hands clapping and little tongues chattering,
And, like fowls in a farmyard when barley is scattering,
Out came the children running.
All the little boys and girls,
With rosy cheeks and flaxen curls,
And sparkling eyes and teeth like pearls,
Tripping and skipping, ran merrily after
The wonderful music with shouting and laughter.

*by **Robert Browning** (1812–1889)*

justling	(jostling) pushing, shoving
pitching	moving vigorously
fowls	hens
flaxen	pale yellow

2 Now answer these questions. Write your answers on a separate piece of paper.

a How would you describe the **rhythm** in this poem?

b Why has the poet created this effect?

3 How has the strong rhythm been created? Give examples from the poem to help explain your ideas.

4 Explain how **rhyme** is used to add to the effect.

5 Read the poem aloud, keeping the rhythm and rhyme, and making the meaning clear.

For help with the questions on this page see
Understanding English: Poetry **pages 6–9.**

Read this extract from the start of a much longer poem.

From **Jabberwocky**

'Twas brillig, and the slithy toves
Did gyre and gimble in the wabe;
All mimsy were the borogoves,
And the mome raths outgrabe.

'Beware the Jabberwock, my son!
The jaws that bite, the claws that catch!
Beware the Jubjub bird, and shun
The frumious Bandersnatch!'

He took his vorpal sword in hand:
Long time the manxome foe he sought –
So rested he by the Tumtum tree,
And stood awhile in thought.

by **Lewis Carroll** *(1832–1898)*

shun	avoid, ignore
foe	enemy
sought	looked for

Now answer these questions. Write your answers on a separate piece of paper.

1 Explain what you think this poem might be about.

2 Find and copy **three made-up words** from the **third verse**.

3 Why do you think the poet chose to use made-up words?

4 **a** Which of these **terms** describe the poem? You can tick **two**.

shape poem ☐   narrative poem ☐

nonsense poem ☐   haiku ☐

b Give reasons for your choices.

5 How is this poem **similar** to 'The Pied Piper' on page 67?

For help with the questions on this page see
Understanding English: Poetry **pages 24, 30, 32, 34 and 36.**

Read these verses from a poem about the seasons.

Seasons

In Springtime when the leaves are young,
Clear dewdrops gleam like jewels, hung
On boughs the fair birds roost among.

In Winter when the birds are gone,
The sun himself looks starved and wan,
And starved the snow he shines upon.

*by **Christina Rossetti** (1830–1894)*

1 Underline any **interesting** and **effective** uses of language that you notice.

2 **a** Find and copy the **simile** used in **verse 1**. _____

  b Why do you think the poet chose this comparison?

  _____

3 **a** Find and copy the example of **personification** used in **verse 2**. _____

  _____

  b What does this line tell us? _____

  _____

Now read these **metaphors**.

Autumn leaves are glowing embers, falling – then dying.
The lone tree in winter – a skeleton's hand, reaching for the sky.

4 Why are autumn leaves described in this way? _____

_____

5 Why is the tree described in this way? _____

_____

For help with the questions on this page see
***Understanding English: Poetry* pages 16–19.**

Poetry Using poetic language

1 Rewrite these simple **similes** as longer **metaphors**, like those on page 69.

a Car headlights are like orange eyes.

_____

b My shadow is like a slither of night.

_____

c The butterfly is like a paintbox.

_____

d Fallen leaves are like scrunched-up brown paper.

_____

2 Write sentences that use **personification** to describe each of the following things.

a an empty house _____

b a wildfire _____

c an old oak tree _____

3 Rewrite these sentences using **alliteration** for effect.

a The owl swoops silently.

_____

b It was a dark day.

_____

c The cat crept.

_____

For help with the questions on this page see
***Understanding English: Poetry* pages 13, 15, 18 and 19.**

Practice

Poetry Responding to a poem

Read this extract two or three times. What **ideas** come into your head? What **pictures** come into your mind?

From **Pleasant sounds**

The rustling of leaves under the feet in woods and under hedges;
The crumpling of cat-ice and snow down wood-rides, narrow lanes, and every street causeway;
Rustling through a wood or rather rushing, while the wind halloos in the oak-top like thunder;
The rustle of birds' wings startled from their nests or flying unseen into the bushes;
The whizzing of larger birds overhead in a wood, such as crows, puddocks, buzzards;
The trample of robins and woodlarks on the brown leaves, and the patter of squirrels on the
    green moss;
    …

by **John Clare** (1793–1864)

cat-ice	thin layer of milky-white ice
puddock	bird of prey

1 Read the poem again. Underline **phrases** or **lines** that you find effective.

Now answer these questions about your thoughts on the poem.

2 What is the poem about? What is the **theme**?

_____

3 Which lines or phrases did you find **effective**? Explain your choices.

_____

_____

_____

4 What did you notice about **how** the poem is written?

_____

_____

_____

5 What is your overall **response** to the poem? Refer to the poem to explain. Write your commentary on a separate piece of paper.

For help with the questions on this page see
Understanding English: Poetry pages 20–23 and 26–27.

Poetry Poems in different forms

1 Here are five poems about **sounds**. Each poem is written in a **different form**. Write the name of the poetic form in the box next to each poem and explain the **key features** that helped you identify it.

a   The wind passes through
Whispering to the tree tops –
See the branches nod.

> This is _____
>
> because _____
>
> _____

b   **S**ea spraying over rocks,
Puddle jumping,
Leaks gushing,
A bath overflowing
Swimmers thrashing
Hose pipes squirting

> This is _____
>
> because _____
>
> _____

c   There was a young man from Dunbar,
Who purchased a brand new car.
It would rattle and rumble
And clatter and grumble
But would never go very far.

> This is _____
>
> because _____
>
> _____

d   Tick tocker
Hour chimer
Seconds chaser
Time passer
Alarm screecher
People waker

> This is _____
>
> because _____
>
> _____

e   trudging
in mud
stomping
in mud
jumping in mud
with a great big …

SQUELCH!

> This is _____
>
> because _____
>
> _____

For help with the questions on this page see
Understanding English: Poetry **pages 32–34 and 36.**

The questions on this page will help you to plan and write your own poem on the theme of **sounds**. It can be any sound – town or country, pleasant or unpleasant, a single sound or a collection.

1 Write down some **ideas** for your poem. Make a note of **descriptive words** or **phrases** that come into your head.

2 Now decide on the **form** for your poem and circle it in the box below.

haiku	cinquain	free verse
shape poem	list poem	acrostic

3 Shape your ideas into your chosen form. Once you are happy with it, write the finished copy of your poem.

Draft

Final version

For help with the questions on this page see
Understanding English: Poetry **pages 33, 35, 37–39.**

Answers

Grammar

Page 4: Nouns and adjectives

1 These are just examples of the sort of precise nouns you might have chosen.
  a The **athlete** went for a <u>run</u> in the <u>park</u>.
  b An angry <u>woman</u> chased her <u>dog</u> around the **department store**.
  c <u>Mr Brown</u> left his <u>book</u> in the **laboratory**.
  d The **tourist** put her new <u>case</u> on the <u>seat</u> of her <u>car</u>.
  e His <u>story</u> about my <u>dog</u> eating the **chocolate éclair** was a <u>lie</u>.

2 These are just examples of the sort of adjectives you might have chosen.
  a a **shadowy** face behind a **dusty** window
  b a pair of **dainty** slippers in front of the **welcoming** fire
  c a **grey** day in **bleak** November
  d a **cosy** cottage in a **picturesque** village

3 There was <u>some</u> bread in <u>the</u> basket and <u>a</u> juicy apple.

These are just examples of the sort of sentences you might have written.

4 The castle had **a wooden drawbridge leading to a rusty portcullis**.

5 Scarface the pirate **was fiercer than an angry tiger**.

6 This ice cream **has the smoothest, crispiest chocolate and the richest caramel centre**.

Page 5: Verbs and adverbs

1 These are just examples of suitable verbs for these sentences.
  a The getaway car **swerved** left and **screeched** to a halt.
  b The flood water **surged** past him as he **struggled** against it.
  c I **crawled** out of bed and **dragged** myself to the bathroom.
  d She **scrambled** up the slope as a rock **plummeted** past her.
  e Yannis **sliced** through the defence and **slammed** the ball into the net.

2 These are just examples of suitable adverbs you might have chosen.
  a Jameela **carefully** opened the box.
  b He held on **grimly**.
  c He **hurriedly** gathered up his papers.
  d She sat down **irritably**.
  e That night he slept **restlessly**.

3 These are just examples of suitable adverbs. Make sure you have used a comma after each one.
  a Clumsily,   **b** Gradually,   **c** Guiltily,   **d** Silently,

4 **a** The squirrel **was** startled and **raced** up the tree.
  b The old man **ate** his dinner and **washed** up.
  c Leaves **fell** from the trees and **fluttered** in the breeze.

Page 6: Cohesion: linking ideas

1 **a** They link the two sentences. They show that the second sentence adds more to what is said in the first sentence.
  b however

2 These are examples of suitable time adverbials. Make sure you have used a comma after each one.
  a Meanwhile,   **c** Eventually,   **e** Next,
  b Suddenly,   **d** As the years passed,

3 These are just examples of the sort of sentences that could follow the adverbials.
  a However, **all was not lost**.
  b On the other hand, **others are thriving**.
  c In contrast, **Charlie seemed fresh as a daisy**.

4 These are just examples. Other adverbials could be used.
  a **As a result,** some homes are without electricity.
  b **Consequently,** farmers are concerned about their crops.

Page 7: Conjunctions

1 **a** though/although/even though   **c** until/unless   **e** after/despite
    b because/as   **d** while

2 **a** The old gentleman smiled <u>when</u> he saw the photograph <u>because</u> it reminded him of happier times.
    b The old gentleman smiled before he left.

3 These are just examples of how the sentences might continue.
  a She left the safety of the cave **although *she knew it was a risk***.
  b The rumble grew louder and louder **until *suddenly it stopped***.
  c There was no way out **unless *someone heard him shouting***.
  d He wiped his eyes **before *he entered the room***.
  e He would open the chest **if *only he could find the key***.
  f The desert seemed endless **but *in the distance she saw the mountains***.

Page 8: Verb tense and agreement

1 I **was watching** television while Mum **was talking** on the phone.

2 **a** On Friday we **caught** the bus.
    b Tomorrow I **will be** up early.
    c He **threw** the ball to me.
    d He had **eaten** already.
    e The window was **broken**.

3 **a** All last week the car **was** being repaired so we **had** to walk.
    b Yesterday, we met Mick and **went** to the park before it **rained**.
    c Saturday was a stormy day so Beth **stayed** indoors and **read**.
    d We found the castle but it **was** closed, so we **came** straight back.

4 **a** I **have** brown hair.
    b We **were** really sorry.
    c These buses **are** always late.
    d I **like** football.
    e There **were** people everywhere.

Page 9: Person and pronouns

1 You might have used other pronouns for some answers, but it must be clear who the pronouns refer to.
  a They were waiting for **their** mother to pick **them** up from swimming.
  b I knew the bag was **mine** because **I** saw **my** name in it.

2 **a** The dog was right behind **her/him** as **she/he** ran towards **her/his** front gate.
    b **They** only moved into **their** new house a week ago, and moving to the country has been a shock for **them** all.

3 the problem

4 Your version does not have to be exactly like this but the meaning must be clear.
Ezra took his dog Rex for a walk in the park. **Ezra** threw a stick and **Rex** bounded after it, wagging his tail. **Rex** stopped and sniffed around the bush where **the stick** had landed, but then **the dog** forgot about **the stick** and set off again. This time **Rex** did not stop. **Ezra** shouted for him to come back – but **Rex** just kept running.

Page 10: One-clause and two-clause sentences

1 These are just examples of the sort of sentences you could write.
   a The clock had stopped ticking.
   b I like milk chocolate best.
   c The door swung open.
   d The old man groaned.
   e There was no time to think.

2 These are just examples of the sort of sentences you might have written.
   a The thief has not been found. **The police are mystified**.
   b Ben did not hear. **The waves were too loud**.

3 **a** I looked around **but** the house was empty **and** silent.
   b He must stay calm **and** concentrate **or** he would make a mistake

4 These are just examples of how you might have completed the sentences.
   a The dog barked and **the boy backed away**.
   b The dog barked but **no-one heard him**.
   c At first she seemed friendly but **then she changed**.
   d He pointed a trembling finger and **everyone turned to look**.
   e Switch the lights off or **someone might see us**.

5 **a** <u>Jenny</u> fell off a wall.
   b <u>The box</u> was on the table.
   c <u>The dog</u> hid the bone.
   d <u>We</u> went to the cinema.

Page 11: Adverbials

1 These are just suggestions – other prepositional phrases could be used.
   a A fire had started **in the wood** *after midnight*.
   b A thick fog descended **over the moors** *during the day*.
   c The two strangers walked together **along the lane** *in the moonlight*.
   d **At tea time,** the boy sat quietly **in the corner of the room**.
   e **In the morning,** he found an enormous pumpkin **at the bottom of the garden**.
   f **On the seventh day,** the King called his advisers **to his chamber**.

2 This is just an example – you may have chosen a different sentence and a different adverb.
Silently, the two strangers walked together along the lane in the moonlight.

3 **a** **Outside,** behind the dustbins, there was a sack of gold.
   b **Slowly,** he raised his hand to the sky.
   c **Excitedly,** the crowd gathered outside the palace./**Outside the palace,** the crowd gathered excitedly.
   d **Gradually, from the purple smoke,** a figure emerged./**From the purple smoke,** a figure gradually emerged./**Gradually,** a figure emerged from the purple smoke.
   e **During the night,** snow fell silently./**Silently,** during the night, snow fell.

Page 12: Clauses

1 These are just examples – there are other ways of combining the sentences.
   a **When** the lamp failed, he tried the torch **but** it just flickered and died.
   b **Picking** up the spade, he dug and dug **until** he was exhausted.
   c **After** they fled the city, they rode for seven nights **before** they reached safety.

2 **a** <u>Mrs Brown gripped her hat</u>, which nearly blew away.
   b Mary hurried to school <u>even when it snowed</u>.
   c The house <u>that was for sale</u> was rather run down.

3 These are just examples – there are many possible sentences.

   a The tiger paused. *Lifting its tail menacingly,* it stared down at the small child *who backed away even further.*

   b Time was running out. *Even though he had made it to the control room,* the safe was still locked and Matt was still trapped.

   c Lightning flashed. *Standing alone on the hillside,* she felt the thunder rumble around her.

   d He wept for joy. *Against all the odds,* he had reached the safety of the island.

Page 13: Moving clauses in a sentence

1   **a** **When the rain came,** he took shelter inside.

   b **Unless we do something,** the library will close next month.

   c **Although I was nervous,** I strode to the front of the class.

   d **As the magician appeared,** the room fell silent.

2 These are just examples of how to add subordinate clauses – you may have used different wording.

   a Start: **As darkness fell**, Ellie began to cry.

   b Middle: Ellie, **tired of walking**, began to cry.

   c End: Ellie began to cry **when she heard the news**.

3 These are just examples – you may have ordered or joined the clauses differently.

   a Mrs Atkins, looking out of her window, saw everything.
      Looking out of her window, Mrs Atkins saw everything.

   b Ignoring the fuss around him, the boy continued to watch cartoons.
      The boy, ignoring the fuss around him, continued to watch cartoons.

   c Although my uncle is eccentric, I always enjoy his visits.
      Although he is eccentric, I always enjoy my uncle's visits.

Page 14: Different types of sentence

1 These are just suggestions for the different sentence types you might have written.

   a Statement: Our rubbish is collected every week.

   b Question: How much rubbish do you throw away each week?

   c Command: Put your rubbish in the bin.

   d Exclamation: What rubbish!

2 These are just suggestions for questions you might use.

   a But was it safe?   **b** Can you help?   **c** What now?   **d** Could you be a winner?

3 These are just examples of the sort of conditional sentences you might write.

   a If I won the lottery, **I would buy my family a new house**.

   b I always do my homework **if Mum reminds me**.

4   **a** The man **was followed** through the darkened streets.

   b The last blueberry muffin **had been eaten**.

   c The plants **were watered** every day.

Page 15: More grammar

1   **a** Isla will come.

   b Of course, she can help.
      She can definitely help.

2   **a** There **are** piles of papers on **those** chairs so no-one has **anywhere** to sit.

   b Sanjay's model **was really** good but Sam's was **better/best**.

   c Dom and **I** found **an** egg **that** had a broken shell.

   d The builder **fell** through **a** hole in **my** roof.

3   **a** You will help, won't you?

   b I would be grateful if you could come to my assistance. (This is just an example to show a formal style of request.)

   c I wish I **were** able to help you, but sadly it is not possible.

4 Sometimes there is not enough time to do everything.

Punctuation

Page 16: Full stops and capital letters

1   Each sentence should start with a capital letter and end with a full stop.

2   **a** All birds have wings. Most birds use their wings to fly.
     b Wait for the milk to boil. Keep stirring all the time.
     c The girl was not listening. She was too busy reading Harry Potter.
     d Let me tell you about my holiday. We went to Spain.
     e No-one was looking. She took Jo's pen from her pocket and scribbled something on the pad.

These are just examples of how you might have used the capital letters.

3   Hari and Ella went shopping on Monday.

4   Amy's birthday is in April and Jacob's is in May.

5   Stella and I start at Havington High in September.

Page 17: Question marks and exclamation marks

1   **a** Is paper made from trees?   **d** Run, run as fast as you can!
     b What a star!   **e** There was silence in the hall.
     c Could Annie have been right?   **f** But what can we do about it?

These are just examples of sentences with question or exclamation marks.

2   Did you see the monkey?

3   The monkey stole my banana!

4   An old man was sitting in his kitchen. He was thinking about his supper. Would he have a bowl of hot soup or leftover fish stew? The old man's stomach rumbled at the thought of food.

    Rat-a-tat-tat! Rat-a-tat-tat! There was a sudden knocking at the door. Who could it be at this time? The man was not expecting company. He got up and hobbled over to the door. He opened the door a crack and peered out. Then he stared in amazement. On his doorstep stood the King! The King in person!

Page 18: Commas

1   These are just examples of where the commas go – you might have added different items.
     a In the picnic basket they found **jam sandwiches, cheese rolls, strawberry tarts, chocolate éclairs and orange juice**.
     b A glance around the storeroom revealed **piles of boxes, empty packing cases, a few paint tins, some tools and a trolley**.
     c For the camping trip, you will need **waterproof clothing, sensible shoes, a sleeping bag, a ground sheet and a torch**.
     d **Lions, leopards, panthers, pumas and tigers** are all types of big cat.

2   **a** I'm waiting for an answer, Tarik.
     b Unfortunately, it was too late.
     c No, we cannot do that.
     d Mum was right, as usual.
     e You will come, won't you?
     f At that moment, the door shut.

3   Later that evening, Gran unpacked her bag. She took out her knitting, her library book, her glasses and a pack of toffees. Carefully, she placed each item on the table. Gran likes to have everything neat and tidy, you see.

Page 19: Apostrophes

1   **a** don't   **f** we'll
     b it's   **g** they've
     c she's   **h** haven't
     d I'd   **i** you'll
     e you're   **j** won't

2 **a** my father's book   **d** the pirates' ship
    b the children's faces   **e** the clowns' hats
    c the referee's whistle   **f** the dinosaur's egg

3 **a** Ami<u>rs</u> gone to Emm<u>as</u> house and I<u>m</u> stuck here.   Amir's, Emma's, I'm
    b The shar<u>ks</u> teeth were bigger than Da<u>ds</u> hand.   shark's, Dad's
    c Ben says th<u>ats</u> why he wo<u>nt</u> play in Kof<u>is</u> team.   that's, won't, Kofi's
    d I was<u>nt</u> surprised when the player<u>s</u> heads dropped.   wasn't, players'

Page 20: Inverted commas

1 These are just examples of where the punctuation in lines of dialogue should go.
    a **'Where have you been?'** demanded Mum.
    b **'I'm the King of the jungle,'** said the lion to the mouse.
    c **'Come back!'** cried Marcus loudly.
    d **'Get out of that car,'** ordered the police sergeant.
    e **'Have you seen any bananas?'** the monkey asked the hippo.
    f The conductor yelled, **'Stop!'**

2 Your wording may differ slightly but the punctuation must be correct. Note the alternatives used for 'said'.
    a **'I will meet you at one o'clock,'** he stated.
    b **'How did you know about the diamonds?'** he asked.
    c **'Go back!'** shouted Rosie.
    d **'I didn't see the red light because of the fog,'** explained the man.

3 **a** The bank robber shouted, "Hand over the money!"
    b "Where are you?" called Meena. "I can't see you."

Page 21: Setting out direct speech

1 'I'm bored,' said Jake.
    'I'm bored too,' muttered Dev with a sigh.
    'I'm so bored I'm bored with being bored,' added Fatima.
    'Well, let's do something then,' replied Jake, standing up suddenly.
    'Like what?' asked Dev.
    'We could go to the park,' suggested Jake.

2 **b** ellipsis
    c because the grasshopper is interrupted
    d 'Sorry,' said the ant. 'I'm much too busy.'

Page 22: Commas and subordinate clauses

1 **a** no comma   **c** comma   **e** comma
    b comma   **d** no comma

2 **b** Exhausted by the events, he fell asleep.
    c She approached the wizard, hoping to find the answer.
    e Although the storm raged, she was safe inside.

3 These are just examples of sentences to show where the comma should be placed.
    a Because the dragon **was sleeping**, *the people felt safe.*
    b Even though the **town centre was busy**, *no-one saw the robbery.*
    c As it was nearly **dark**, *they made their way back to the farm.*
    d Surprised by **the sudden attack**, *they were soon trapped.*
    e Storming through **the field**, *he took the lead.*

4 **a** Slowly, he crept down the corridor. Holding the lamp high, he felt along the wall.

b Setting off once more, the traveller quickened her pace. She knew that time was running out, yet she was still far from home.

c When the race began, everyone set off enthusiastically. Full of energy, they sprinted across the field.

d The twins carried four plates, each piled high with sandwiches.

Page 23: Comma or full stop?

1 **a** incorrect   **c** correct   **e** incorrect
      b correct   **d** incorrect   **f** correct

2 **a** It was time to leave. They put on their overcoats.

d It was nearly noon. We were going to miss the train.

e Samson's field is a special place. It must not be spoilt.

3 **a** It was a stormy day. The wind roared down the chimney. Rain splattered the window.

b She watched, scared to move. She had never seen a motor car before, never even heard one.

c Frantically, she ran down the corridor, slipping and stumbling. She had to escape.

d After a long time, when the smoke finally cleared, Simon found himself standing on a cliff-top. He was quite alone. Marsha had vanished.

Page 24: Commas, brackets and dashes

1 These are examples of how to use commas for parenthesis.

a Chioma, **breathing heavily**, crossed the finishing line.

b Mr Singh, **who lives nearby**, was first on the scene.

c The owl, **sitting on a high branch**, watched them carefully.

d Tess, **excited by the thought**, was the first to volunteer.

2 **a** Fry the onions until soft (two to three minutes) before adding the herbs

b In the wardrobe he kept shoes (red, silver and gold) and matching hats.

c You can feed birds with kitchen leftovers (bread, cake, apple cores, bacon rind) in the winter months.

d Mrs Slater (the headteacher) spoke to Class 6.

3 These are just examples of the sort of surprising or dramatic things you might add.

a Maybe they had been captured – **maybe not.**

b Mia recognised the smell at once – **the smell of danger.**

c I like the look of these young earthlings – **they look delicious.**

d The sack was stuffed with something – **twenty-pound notes!**

4 This is just an example of how you might use two dashes to add extra information into a sentence.

a She let out a scream – **a piercing shriek** – and raced out of the room.

b There was a spider – **the biggest ever** – sitting in the bath.

c Mr Green – **our neighbour** – is very stern.

d It was cold – **freezing, in fact** – so we stayed inside.

Page 25: Colons, semicolons and hyphens

1 These are just examples of the sort of things that can follow a colon.

a He read the name on the envelope: **Mr R. Jenkins**.

b Bread has only four main ingredients: **flour, yeast, salt and water**.

c I have just one motto in life: **honesty is the best policy**.

2 **a** No-one else was in the room; I was quite alone.

b The first book was good; the others were disappointing.

c I did not go out; it was too cold.

3 **a** This story has it all: an exotic setting, a thrilling adventure and an unbelievable ending.
  b Some people like city living; others prefer life in the country.

4 A crowd was forming, with **grown-ups** and children, **wide-eyed** toddlers and curious **passers-by**, all straining to see.

Vocabulary

Page 26: Word meanings

1 The wording of your definitions may be slightly different.
  a **compulsory** a must, required, not optional
  b **desolate** deserted, bleak
  c **buffeted** battered, blew (them) about
  d **brandished** waved with a flourish
  e **infuriatingly** annoyingly, maddeningly
  f **dispel** banish

2
permanent — fixed or lasting
reinforced — made stronger
identical — the same in every detail
opaque — not clear or transparent

3 We reinforced the structure to make it permanent. (This is just an example of the sort of sentence you might write.)

4 The wording of your definitions may be slightly different.
  a **recline** lie back
  b **contemplate** consider, think
  c **anthology** collection of poems or stories
  d **conceal** hide
  e **sufficient** enough
  f **remote** far away
  g **modify** change, adapt

Page 27: Word roots

1 **a** press **d** public **g** class
  b joy **e** act **h** sign
  c script **f** obey **i** muscle

2 These are just examples – there are other possibilities.
  a **part** particle, partition, partial, partly
  b **act** actor, activity, action, react

3 These are just examples – there are other possibilities.
  a **aero** aerobatics, aeroplane, aerobics, aerosol
  b **aqua** aqualung, aquamarine, aquarium, aquatic
  c **audi** audible, audience, audition, auditorium
  d **tri** triangle, trident, trio, tripod
  e **super** superlative, superhuman, supermarket, supernatural

4 **a** **sub** under/below/beneath **d** **inter** between
  b **port** carry **e** **bi** two
  c **ex** out

Page 28: Homographs

1   **a** ring   **b** light   **c** form   **d** tug

2   **a pupil**   the middle part of the eye; a schoolchild or someone being taught
     b watch   to look at or observe; a device for telling the time
     c club   a group of people with a shared interest; a weapon or heavy stick

3   **a** bat, crane   **b** pop, jam   **c** table, book

4   These are just examples – you may have written other sentences.
     a stable (noun)   The horses were in the **stable**.
        stable (adjective)   The bridge was **stable** even in high winds.
     b rock (noun)   An enormous **rock** blocked the entrance to the cave.
        rock (verb)   The boat began to **rock** from side to side.
     c mean (adjective)   The tax collector was a **mean** man.
        mean (verb)   What do you **mean** by that?

Page 29: Synonyms

1   **a** easy, simple, uncomplicated, straightforward
     b pour, gush, stream, spurt
     c tidy, neat, organised, orderly
     d pull, drag, haul, tug
     e lean, slender, thin, slight

2   These are just examples – you may have chosen other synonyms.
     a It was a **boring** event.   dull, dreary, unexciting, tedious
     b The crowd were **excited**.   thrilled, exhilarated, enthusiastic, exuberant
     c It is **hot** here.   scalding, scorching, sizzling, sweltering
     d The dish was **tasty**.   delicious, appetising, mouthwatering, flavoursome
     e It is **quiet** inside.   peaceful, undisturbed, tranquil, calm
     f He went for a **quick** run.   swift, brisk, speedy, hasty

3   This is just an example – you may have chosen other synonyms or used them in different places.
     With a **dreadful** howl, the **vile** creature rose out of the swamp. A **repulsive** smell filled the air.
     I caught just a glimpse of its **grotesque** features.

Page 30: Choosing the best word

1   **a** springs   **b** bounds/leaps   **c** vaults   **d** hops/leaps

2   **a** dined   **b** devoured   **c** munched   **d** consumed

3   **a** massive   **b** towering   **c** vast/gigantic   **d** colossal/gigantic

4   These are just examples – there are alternative words you could have chosen.
     a irritable → bad-tempered
     b nervous → terrified

Page 31: Antonyms

1   **a** arrive   **depart/leave**   **f** curved   **straight**
     b weak   **strong**   **g** imaginary   **real**
     c stale   **fresh**   **h** question   **answer**
     d friend   **enemy**   **i** help   **hinder**
     e absent   **present**   **j** guilty   **innocent**

2   **a** **un**do   **f** **im**mature   **k** **ir**regular
     b **im**passable   **g** **in**sensitive   **l** **in**sufficient
     c **dis**like/**un**like   **h** **un**healthy   **m** **dis**agree
     d **non**-fiction   **i** **in**active   **n** **dis**honest
     e **un**acceptable   **j** **dis**approve   **o** **un**usual

3　**a** Tom is the best runner and Harry is the **worst**. Tom will win and Harry will **lose**.

　　b Some people are wise and others are **foolish**. Some people are right and others are **wrong**.

　　c You have many talents and he has **few**. But he is hard-working and you are **lazy**.

　　d This car is old and that one is **new**. This car is slow and that one is **quick/fast**.

Page 32: Prefixes and suffixes

1　These are just examples – you may have come up with alternative words.
If your words are not listed, check them in a dictionary or ask an adult.

　　a **un**law**ful**　　　　　　　　　　　**g** **dis**agree**able**/**dis**agree**ment**

　　b **un**employ**ment**/**un**employ**able**,　　**h** **mis**manage**ment**/**un**manage**able**
　　　　re-employ**ment**　　　　　　　　　**i** **im**person**al**

　　c **un**avoid**able**　　　　　　　　　　**j** **dis**order**ly**

　　d **re**turn**able**　　　　　　　　　　　**k** **in**complete**ly**/**in**complete**ness**

　　e **un**willing**ly**/**un**willing**ness**　　　**l** **un**help**ful**

　　f **re**place**ment**/**re**place**able**

2　**a** crisp**y**　　　　　**e** break**able**　　　　**i** tradition**al**

　　b bend**y**　　　　　**f** enjoy**able**　　　　**j** mass**ive**

　　c pain**ful**/pain**less**　**g** end**less**　　　　**k** emotion**al**

　　d peace**ful**/peace**able**　**h** spot**less**/spot**ty**　**l** taste**less**/taste**ful**/tast**y**

3　**a** The farm**er** was known throughout the king**dom** for his fair**ness**, honest**y** and truth**fulness**.

　　b The manag**er** said that hope**fully** the team would be more success**ful** next season and win the champion**ship**.

　　c The state**ment** was critic**al** of the driver's behaviour; it said the accident was entire**ly** avoid**able**.

　　d We use only the fresh**est** ingredients, season**al** vegetables and local**ly** grown organ**ic** produce.

Page 33: Old and new words

1　espied, doubloons, settle, frockcoat

2　multimedia, stream, audio, video, interface, downloads, online

3　Old words with a new meaning: tweet, tablet, wicked, spam, wireless, text
Words made by blending two existing words: sitcom, carjacking, dancercise, fantabulous, camcorder, brunch

4　**a** judo, skiing, sumo　　　　　　　**c** emu, gnu, tarantula

　　b pizza, chapatti, coleslaw　　　　　**d** kimono, dungarees, sombrero

Page 34: New words and onomatopoeia

1　**a** <u>celebs</u> and <u>VIPs</u> only　　　celebrities; very important persons/people

　　b the <u>DJ</u>'s <u>limo</u>　　　　　　disk jockey; limousine

　　c download <u>apps</u> and <u>e-books</u>　applications; electronic books

　　d <u>CCTV</u> on Park <u>Ave</u>　　　　closed-circuit television; Avenue

2　These are just examples of suitable onomatopoeic words – you might have chosen different ones.

　　a Splat!　　　　**b** Smash!　　　　**c** Creak …　　　　**d** Whoosh!

3　plip, plop, splatter, splosh (These are just examples – you might have written other words.)

4　**a** **staycation**　　holiday staying at home

　　b **travelator**　　moving walkway

　　c **spellathon**　　spelling competition

　　d **guesstimate**　very rough estimate

　　e **chillax**　　　rest and relax

　　f **cybercrime**　crimes committed using computers or the internet

Page 35: Formal and informal words

1 Personal diary: brainwave, gizmo, snag, nifty, my mate
Formal letter: concept, device, complication, ingenious, my associate

2 These are just examples – you may have come up with alternative words.

a	**to throw away**	dispose of, discard, dispense with
b	**to tell someone**	inform, advise, notify
c	**to get**	obtain, acquire, receive
d	**horrible**	unpleasant, offensive, appalling
e	**fussy**	selective, particular, demanding

3 These are just examples of the sort of sentences you might write.

a It was a formal occasion.
b I did not understand the significance./I did not receive it.
c The business collapsed.
d He had to confess/admit his guilt/mistake.

Spelling

Page 36: Tricky letter strings

1
a h**ear**d, s**ear**ch, l**ear**n, **ear**th
b trea**sure**, plea**sure**, lei**sure**, mea**sure**
c flav**our**, rum**our**, col**our**, fav**our**ite
d spec**ial**, soc**ial**, offic**ial**, artific**ial**
e p**aus**e, c**aus**e, bec**aus**e, appl**aus**e

2 **a** thought **b** bought **c** brought **d** fought

3 These are just examples – you might have written other words.
a word, work, worst
b weight, eighty, eighth

4
a would, could
b tough, enough
c found, ground
d notice, office
e sure, nervous
f people, believed
g future, station

Page 37: Tricky letters

1
a stoma**ch**
b s**y**mbol
c **ph**antom
d g**u**ide
e gra**ph**
f ma**ch**ine
g **ech**o
h s**y**stem
i **ch**ef
j **rh**yme
k **ph**rase
l **y**a**ch**t

2
a Lemons are <u>biter</u>. bitter
b The children had <u>super</u>. supper
c I can use <u>comas</u>. commas

3
a **w**ritten
b num**b**
c **g**nash
d **k**neel
e **wh**isper
f cas**t**le
g clim**b**ing
h **w**restling
i dou**b**t
j **w**riggle

4
a voi**c**e, silen**c**e
b re**c**ently, ex**c**iting
c **c**entre, ri**g**id
d chan**g**e, intelli**g**ent

Page 38: Syllables and compound words

1 teapot, uphill, popcorn, dustbin, desktop

2
a track + s**ui**t		**f** he**ar**t + burn
b cl**oa**k + room		**g** c**ou**nt + down
c w**a**ter + fall		**h** cup + b**oar**d
d ha**l**f + time		**i** mot**or** + bike
e wa**l**k + way		**j** qua**r**ter + back

3 Examples include: anybody, somebody, everybody, nobody, bodywork

4
a trumpet **2**	**e** shampoo **2**	**i** combination **4**
b holiday **3**	**f** family **3**	**j** hotel **2**
c calendar **3**	**g** brilliant **3**	**k** important **3**
d helicopter **4**	**h** extraordinary **6**	**l** activity **4**

5
a chim/**pan**/zee	**d** kan/**ga**/roo	**g** pel/**i**/can
b cat/**er**/**pil**/lar	**e** al/**li**/**ga**/tor	**h** buf/**fa**/lo
c fla/**min**/go	**f** but/**ter**/fly	**i** sal/**a**/**man**/der

Page 39: Adding prefixes and suffixes

1
a incorrect	**d** correct	**g** incorrect
b correct	**e** incorrect	**h** correct
c correct	**f** incorrect	**i** incorrect

2 always, disappear, immature, antifreeze, nonsense

3
a smoker, smokeless, smoky
b tuneful, tuneless, tuner
c likely, likeness, liken
d lonely, loner, lonesome

4
a plen**tiful**	**d** joy**ful**	**g** happ**ily**	**j** enjoy**able**
b beau**tiful**	**e** happ**iness**	**h** hungr**ily**	**k** var**ious**
c fanc**iful**	**f** laz**iness**	**i** rel**iable**	**l** histor**ic**

Page 40: Unstressed vowels

1
a math**e**matics	**e** popul**a**r	**i** gener**a**l
b librar**y**	**f** hospit**a**l	**j** sever**a**l
c hist**o**ry	**g** gramm**a**r	**k** simil**a**r
d Janu**a**ry	**h** mis**e**rable	**l** separ**a**te

2
a mar/**vel**/lous	**c** dif/**fer**/ent	**e** deaf/**en**/ing
b Feb/**ru**/ary	**d** cor/**rid**/or	

3
a fright**e**ning	**c** prob**a**bly	**e** desp**e**rate
b gen**e**rous	**d** off**e**ring	**f** int**e**rested

4 import<u>a</u>nt defin<u>i</u>te av<u>e</u>rage ordin<u>a</u>ry sent<u>e</u>nce

Page 41: Homophones

1
a flower and **flour**		**f** who's and **whose**
b steal and **steel**		**g** not and **knot**
c guest and **guessed**		**h** main and **mane**
d right and **write**		**i** key and **quay**
e seen and **scene**		**j** cereal and **serial**

2
a It was as <u>plane</u> as the <u>knows</u> on my face.   plain, nose
b The <u>bare</u> in the zoo looked <u>board</u>.   bear, bored
c Water was <u>leeking</u> from a <u>whole</u>.   leaking, hole
d <u>Brake</u> off a <u>peace</u> of bread.   Break, piece
e I <u>new</u> it would be a <u>grate</u> event.   knew, great

3 These are just examples of sentences you might have written.
a I **ate** a sandwich at **eight** o'clock.
b I **threw** the ball **through** the hoop.
c He **heard** a **herd** of buffalo approaching.
d We weren't **allowed** to read **aloud**.

4 <u>Their</u> were <u>two</u> many stars <u>too</u> count.   There, too, to

Page 42: Adding –s and –es

1
a glass**es**
b group**s**
c chorus**es**
d heart**s**
e g**ee**se
f touch**es**
g bruise**s**
h echo**es**
i answer**s**
j wom**e**n

2
a two countr**ies**
b two cop**ies**
c two stor**ies**
d two pupp**ies**
e two journey**s**
f two repl**ies**
g two bugg**ies**
h two trolley**s**
i two donkey**s**
j two cit**ies**
k two lorr**ies**
l two arm**ies**

3
a The **elves** danced along the **shelves**.
b The **wives** took the **calves** to market.
c The **thieves** wore **scarves** (*or* **scarfs**).

4 For my birthday I had ten balloon**s**, nine ice loll**ies**, eight fruit loa**ves**, seven badge**s**, six tedd**ies**, five pair**s** of shoe**s**, four magic fish**es** (or **fish**), three money box**es**, two gold watch**es** and one bag of rub**ies**.

Page 43: Adding –ed and –ing

1
a build**ing**
b surpris**ing**
c hug**ging**
d carry**ing**
e plan**ning**
f creat**ing**
g admit**ting**
h suggest**ing**
i win**ning**
j writ**ing**
k scatter**ing**
l enjoy**ing**
m welcom**ing**
n consider**ing**
o propel**ling**

2

Present	Past	Present	Past
impress	**impressed**	regret	**regretted**
stop	**stopped**	divide	**divided**
decide	**decided**	obey	**obeyed**
reply	**replied**	carry	**carried**
admit	**admitted**	glance	**glanced**
scamper	**scampered**	frighten	**frightened**
command	**commanded**	topple	**toppled**
study	**studied**	equip	**equipped**

3
a Leav**ing** the trolley, the woman grab**bed** her shop**ping** and dash**ed** out of the supermarket.
b Startl**ed** by the sudden boom, Amit drop**ped** to the ground, his heart rac**ing**.
c The creatures hurr**ied** and scurr**ied** here and there, explor**ing** every surface and search**ing** in every hole.

Page 44: Tricky word endings 1

1
a sensa**tion**
b occa**sion**
c fero**cious**
d offi**cial**

e cau**tious**
f essen**tial**
g men**tion**

2
a reduc**tion**
b crea**tion**
c exclu**sion**
d persua**sion**
e construc**tion**
f distrac**tion**
g discu**ssion**

h progre**ssion**
i exten**sion**
j conclu**sion**
k produc**tion**
l infec**tion**
m explo**sion**
n posse**ssion**

3
a de/**fin**/i/**tion**
b com/**pe**/ti/**tion**

c punc/**tu**/a/**tion**
d in/**for**/ma/**tion**

Page 45: Tricky word endings 2

1
a avoid**able**
b imposs**ible**
c remark**able**
d terr**ible**
e change**able**
f valu**able**
g ed**ible**

h predict**able**
i avail**able**
j invis**ible**
k horr**ible**
l regret**table**
m accept**able**
n reason**able**

2
a trickle, trouble
b label, model
c candles, magical

d hesitant, reluctant
e original, metal
f apparently, frequent

3
a I recieved a brief note from my nieghbour.   rec**ei**ved, n**ei**ghbour
b A feirce blow pierced the sheild.   fi**e**rce, sh**ie**ld
c I beleive my freind may have been deceitful.   bel**ie**ve, fr**ie**nd
d The thief shreiked as he fell through the cieling.   shr**ie**ked, c**ei**ling
e Each peice of news brought grief or releif.   pi**e**ce, rel**ie**f

Fiction

Many of the answers given in this section are examples only – your answers should be similar but may be worded differently.

Page 46: Character clues

1 'a pale, tallow creature'; 'wanting two fingers of the left hand'; 'wore a cutlass'; 'did not look much like a fighter'; 'a smack of the sea about him'.

2 He sounds a bit frightening/unpleasant (reasons should refer to details from above).

3 No, because he seems reluctant to step closer to the man.

4 He is trying to seem friendly (for example, he calls the boy 'sonny') but he says it with 'a kind of leer', which makes him sound unfriendly.

5 He is only pretending to be pleasant; really, he is dangerous. He doesn't trust the boy (Jim). He is there to find/catch someone.

Page 47: Creating characters

1–2 Use details about appearance to show character; use suitable adjectives (for example, warm, sunny smile); use powerful verbs (for example, lurked).

3–4 Show character through what the character says and how it is said; choose verbs and adverbs to use in place of 'said'.

5 Show the character's motives through his/her actions; use powerful verbs and adverbs.

Page 48: Settings

1 No. It sounds bleak and unwelcoming.

2 'Grey-coloured woods'; 'the general colouring was uniform and sad'

3 It makes you feel uneasy – you think that something bad might happen there.

4 'grey, melancholy woods'; 'wild stone spires'; 'surf … foaming and thundering'

5 Use details to create a picture of an idyllic setting; include sights and sounds. Use precise nouns (for example, coconut trees, coral reefs), phrases with adjectives (for example, crescent-shaped beaches of powdery white sand) and powerful verbs and adverbs (for example, blue waves lapped gently).

Page 49: Different points of view

1 Told in the first person, from Jim's point of view.

2 Uses 'I' to refer to the boy. The stranger is described through Jim's eyes – he is a stranger because Jim does not know who he is. We get Jim's impressions and feelings.

3 It puts you on Jim's side. You feel the same as Jim does about the stranger. You don't know who he is either, so there is a sense of mystery.

4 I am frightened of the man. I don't trust him.

5 The young lad looked mighty suspicious. He watched me like a hawk as he wiped the tankard with his napkin. When he went to get the rum, I signalled him over. I thought a bit of friendly conversation would soften him up.

Page 50: Creating effects

1 Scared, worried, on edge because you are waiting for something to happen.

2 **b** to build suspense and tension

3 **a** Uses descriptive language to set a scary mood (for example, 'in the silent frosty air'); describes worrying sounds (for example, 'the tap-tapping'; 'the bolt rattling').
b Creates doubts and uncertainty; focus on sounds rather than seeing; detailed description to delay and build up tension; includes thoughts and feelings of the narrator.

4 Make sure you have used the techniques listed in question 3.

Page 51: Plotting the main events

1 Jim finds a treasure map in an old sailor's sea chest.
Jim sets sail to find the island where the treasure is hidden.
Jim discovers the ship's crew are pirates who also want the treasure.
Jim and his allies have a long battle with the pirates.
Jim, with help from his friends, outwits the pirates and locates the treasure.
Jim returns home safely with his share of the treasure.

Page 52: Traditional story themes and features

1 **a** greedy because he wanted more and more gold
b foolish because he didn't think of the consequences of his actions

2 Be careful what you wish for: there are more important things in life than wealth/gold.

3 **a** Characters: a foolish king; a god
b Setting: the past; a palace
c Events: granting of a wish; magical golden touch
d Themes: learning wisdom/a lesson about life; greed and foolishness leading to bad consequences

Page 53: Plotting and retelling a story

1 It is the moment when the King begins to realise that there are more important things in life than gold. Before this he cared only about gold, but afterwards he realises that things such as food and family are more important.

2 Check that your story follows the same pattern as 'The Golden Touch'. It must have a 'turning point' event that changes the main character.

Page 54: Genre 1

1 Genre: fable
Recognisable features: animal character behaves like a human; foolish
Prediction: blackbird will learn her lesson; story will end with a moral

2 Genre: ghost/horror story
Recognisable features: setting – moors on a foggy night; scary noises with no explanation
Prediction: narrator will be trapped on the moor on a foggy night, will hear the sounds – will perhaps encounter something

3 Genre: detective mystery/whodunnit
Recognisable features: a crime committed; main character – a detective
Prediction: detective will visit the crime scene, look for clues, interview suspects and eventually find the emerald

Page 55: Genre 2

1 **a** adventure
b exciting events with lots of cliffhangers and problems to overcome; a hero and a villain to overcome; a reward at the end; travelling to different places

2 Space commander Jim Hawkins discovers a **plan to destroy the planet Earth**.
He sets off **on the space shuttle to the furthest galaxy where the Klax space station is based**.
There he must outwit **the fearsome Klax warriors and their deadly robots**.
Only then can he **return to Earth, once it is safe**.

3 Your answer to this written task will be individual – check that your ideas fit your chosen genre.

Non-fiction

Many of the answers given in this section are examples only – alternative answers may also be correct.

Page 56: Reading for information

1 to pass on information about different types of traditional games

Page 57: Finding information

1 By grouping the games into different types (skipping games, chasing games, ball games) and then having a section and subheading for each type.

2 They are names of games and the writer wants to make them stand out.

3

Type of activity	Equipment needed	Example games
Skipping games	short ropes	Double Dutch, Can-can, Double skipping
	long rope	Under the moon and over the stars, Criss cross
Chasing games	none	Tig, Tag, Touch, It What's the time, Mr Wolf? Stuck in the mud
Ball games	small balls	Dropsies, Clapsies, Piggy in the middle
	large, light balls	Dodgeball, Big side

4 Piggy in the middle —————— needs a marked area of play
   Criss cross ———————— a ball game for at least three children
   Dodgeball —————————— a skipping game requiring two turners

5 subheadings to find relevant sections; names of games in bold

Page 58: Organising ideas

1 Check: Main heading says what the report is about; information is organised into sections with examples grouped together (for example, 'pretend games' – X Factor, Dr Who, Harry Potter); each section has a subheading (for example, 'Pretend games', 'Ball games').

2 Check: Introduction tells the reader what the report is about.

3 Check: Subheading should say what the section is about. First sentence should introduce the topic with a general or interesting piece of information.

Page 59: Following instructions

1 Yes. There is a clear set of steps and they explain exactly what to do.

2 They are parts where the reader might go wrong or be unsure, so it helps clarify exactly what to do. Italic type is used to make these sentences stand out.

3 Yes or no, but you must give a reason. For example, the steps are clear and easy to follow; *or* a new user might not understand terms such as icon, installer.

4 Similar: tells you what to do; a series of steps to be performed; separate bullet points
   Different: recipe would start with a list of ingredients; different technical language

Page 60: Reading accounts

1 **a** personal
   b The writer is describing something that happened to him/her: uses 'I' and 'we'; lots of personal detail and comments.

2 Lucky socks were in the wash.

3 Events to include: 10.00 – set off; around 10.05–10.35 – stuck in traffic; 10.50 – arrive at ground; around 10.55 – Rick and Dipak arrive; 11.00 kick-off.

Page 61: Comparing accounts

1 Falcons equalised through Elliott in the 78th minute and then Smith scored their winner in the last minute.

2 because it sounds exciting and says what the story is about

3 It's not personal; its purpose is to tell the reader about the match, so it gives more factual detail about what happened; it's not biased. You may also mention differences in structure (for example, the headline/overview of the story) and language (for example, more formal, using players' surnames).

Page 62: Writing accounts

1 Check: Include detail about who, when, what and how; end with a comment, summary or look to the future; use news/sports report style and language.

2–3 Check: Describe events in chronological order, include personal details and feelings; comment on events; keep to a personal informal style and tone.

Page 63: Explaining information

1 because your lungs are working harder to get more oxygen into your body

2 The heart pumps blood round your body.

3 because your body is trying to cool you down

4 The series of text boxes around an illustration helps break up the information into smaller chunks; shows the series of linked events; helps you to picture and relate.

5 to show the order in which they are to be read – a series of linked events

Page 64: Reading critically

1 'The greatest adventure game yet!' 'you'll believe you're really there!'

2 'amazing interactive world'; 'action-packed adventure'; 'spectacular 3-D'

3 to reassure parents who might have concerns about children playing games

4 use of questions ('Can you save the planet?'); addressing the reader directly ('Choose your character'); imperatives that invite ('get playing!'); use of fun or exciting image

Page 65: Comparing views

1 **a** You cannot tell.
b both sides of the argument presented fairly; uses phrases like 'many critics', 'Other people'

2 **a** Points for: train the brain; must move with the times
b Points against: anti-social (that is, played alone rather than with others); waste too much time; harm the brain; bad for the body

3 **a** evidence to support the claim that video games help train the brain
b evidence to illustrate the importance of active, traditional-style play

Poetry

Page 66: Rhyme

1 light, night-light; light, night, tonight; night-light, light, slight, light; moonlight, white, bright

2 First four lines are rhyming couplets; then there is a line between the two rhymes.

3 Most likely examples: you, door

4 This is just an example of how you might have used rhyme to complete the poem.
Bridge across the river wide / **Take me to the other side**.
Beneath your arch the waters flow / **Swirling darkly far below**.

Page 67: Rhythm and reading aloud

2 **a** lively, bouncy, brisk, breathless, relentless, keeps going
b because it sounds lively and bustling like the children skipping along

3 Points to include: list-like pattern with lots of short phrases creates rhythmic beat (for example, 'Small feet were pattering, wooden shoes clattering'); one long sentence makes it relentless – no stopping; repeated stress of –ing verb endings emphasises the rhythm (for example, 'merry crowds justling at pitching and hustling')

4 Rhymes within lines help emphasise the rhythm (for example, 'There was a rustling, that seemed like a bustling'). Three lines all end with the same rhyme (for example, 'girls', 'curls', 'pearls') to drive the rhythm on.

Page 68: Comparing poems

1 It's a quest to find an imaginary creature called the Jabberwock.

2 vorpal, manxome, Tumtum (tree)

3 because it sounds funny and it is a humorous poem

4 **a** nonsense poem; narrative poem
b Nonsense poem: It sounds funny and includes made-up nonsense words.
Narrative poem: It is like the start of a story about a quest to find the Jabberwock.

5 Both are narrative poems/long poems that tell stories; both have strong rhythm and rhyme.

Page 69: Figurative language

1 There are many examples you might have underlined.

2 **a** 'Clear dewdrops gleam like jewels'
b It makes the dewdrops decorative/beautiful and special.

3 **a** 'The sun himself looks starved and wan ...'
b It describes the paleness/weakness/thinness of the sun in winter by comparing it to a sick, starving person.

4 The colours are the same as fire; they are like little specks of fire; they will dry up and die.

5 The branches are thin and bare like a skeleton's bones; it makes it sound cold and lifeless; it describes the shape of the branches against the sky.

Page 70: Using poetic language

These are just examples of how you might use metaphors, personification and alliteration for effect.

1 **a** Car headlights are orange eyes, staring into the darkness – never blinking.
b My shadow – a slither of night, playing hide and seek with the day.
c The butterfly is a paintbox, opening up to reveal its glorious colours.
d Fallen leaves are scrunched-up brown paper blowing in the breeze.

2 **a** Deserted, alone, the house is left with no smile, just its memories.
b Angry fire rages and spits his fury at all.
c Crooked and creaking, the old man of the woods nods knowingly.

3 **a** On soft wings, she silently swoops in a still, soundless sky.
b It was a dull, damp, dark December day.
c Cautiously, calmly, the cat crept down the cold corridor.

Page 71: Responding to a poem

1 There are many lines and phrases you might have underlined. You will have written your thoughts on the poem (there are no 'right' answers) – referring to the poem to explain and justify your opinions.

2 Refer to what the poet was trying to convey (for example, appreciating the sounds of nature).

3 Comment on poetic language; explain why it was effective.

4 You might comment on the structure (for example, like a list poem) or on the fact that there is no rhyme.

5 You might say what you like or dislike about the poem, and explain why. You might comment on the vocabulary used and all the different words used to describe the sounds. You might mention the structure of the poem, which is like a long list of sounds.

Page 72: Poems in different forms

1 **a** Haiku: three lines; one sentence; syllable pattern of 5, 7, 5 syllables
b Acrostic: first letters of each line spelling out the subject
c Limerick: funny; five lines; begins 'There was a young man ...'; lines 1, 2 and 5 rhyme, as do 3 and 4
d List poem/riddle/kenning: give(s) two-word clues about the subject without saying what it is
e Shape poem: words written to fit the shape of the subject

Page 73: Writing poems in different forms

1–3 Check: Express your ideas to the reader; use carefully chosen words; include poetic language (for example, effective imagery, alliteration); use features of your chosen poem form.
For help with this, check that you have used the features and language found in the example poems on page 78.